The Basis of Measurement

Volume 2
Metrication and Current Practice

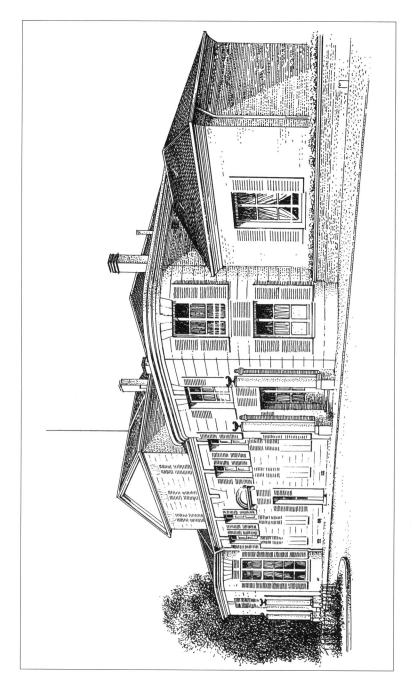

Frontispiece A1 – Pavillion de Breteuil, Bureau International des Poids et Mesures, Sèvres.

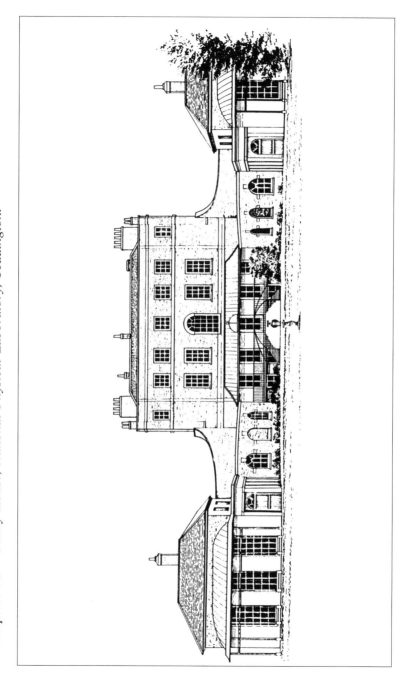

Frontispiece A2 – Bushy House, National Physical Laboratory, Teddington.

The Basis of Measurement

Volume 2
Metrication and Current Practice

By:
Thomas McGreevy MScTech, BSc, CEng, FIEE
Honorary Fellow of the University of Portsmouth

Extended and Edited by:
Peter Cunningham BSc(Lond), DMS(CNAA), Chartered Biologist
Formerly Senior Lecturer at the University of Portsmouth

The Basis of Measurement
Main text © 1997 Thomas McGreevy
Additions and extensions © 1997 Peter Cunningham
First published in 1997
Picton Publishing (Chippenham) Limited
ISBN 0 948251 84 0

Designed and typeset in Times Roman from Editor's discs by
Carnegie Publishing Ltd
18 Maynard Street, Preston PR2 2AL
Printed and bound in the United Kindom by
Picton Publishing (Chippenham) Limited
Queensbridge Cottages, Patterdown,
Chippenham, Wiltshire SN15 2NS

order enquiries
P. Cunningham
72 Swanage Road
SOUTHEND-ON-SEA
SS2 5HY ENGLAND
Tel: 01702 600462

PICTON PUBLISHING (CHIPPENHAM) LIMITED

The Basis of Measurement, Volume 1 Historical Aspects,
is published by the same Author and Editor.

**Each volume of the publication may be used in its own right,
and each may appeal to different groups of readers**

The author is of height 1·75 metres and has a mass of 73 kilograms.

His normal chest measurement is 97 centimetres.

Two paces of his footsteps cover a distance of 1·44 metres.

Contents

List of Tables   xi

List of Illustrations   xiii

List of Appendices   xv

General Acknowledgements   xvii

Personal Acknowledgements   xviii

Preface   xix

Editor's Preface and Acknowledgements   xxi

Chapter V Part 1
    The International System of Units (SI)
    The Seven Base Units   201

Chapter V Part 2
    Prefixes and Suffixes for SI Units   222

Chapter V Part 3
    The SI System of Units – Codes of Practice   237

Chapter VI
    Some Useful Derived Units in SI   246

Chapter VII Part 1
    Metrication in The United Kingdom 1838 – 1939   276

Chapter VII Part 2
        Metrication in The United Kingdom 1939 – 1972   287

Chapter VII Part 3
        Metrication in The United Kingdom 1972 – 1995   311

Chapter VIII
        The North American Scene   325

Chapter IX
        Final Observations   343

Appendices (see separate list, page xv)

References and Further Reading Volume 1 and 2   419

Index of Persons   Volume 2   431

Index of named units   Volume 1 and 2   433

General index   Volume 2   437

Tables – Volume 2

(Tables I–X appear in Volume 1)
Note: for conversion tables – see Appendices pp 366–390

Table		page
XI	The seven SI base units	203
XII	Equivalent values of various calorie units in joules	214
XIII	c.g.s. units with special names	243
XIV	Other units generally deprecated	244
XV	Units used temporarily with the International System	244
XVI	Units used with the International System, obtained experimentally	245
XVII	Thermal resistance of certain materials	248
XVIII	Tog ratings of quilts	248
XIX	Half-lives of certain radio-isotopes	259
XX	Equivalent values of tyre pressures	269
XXI	Efficacies of various filament lamps	272
XXII	Approximate magnitudes of various light sources	275
XXIII	ISO range of paper sizes	323
XXIV	Photographic printing paper sizes	324

XXV   American 'penny nails'   340

XXVI   Fuel consumption equivalents UK (values rounded)   353

XXVII   Fuel consumption equivalents USA (values rounded)   353

XXVIII   Table of equivalent body weights   356

XXIX   Large numbers, UK convention   357

XXX   Large numbers, USA convention   357

XXXI   pH values of certain aqueous liquids   412

XXXII   pH values of reference standard solutions   412

XXXIII   Dimensional formulae of common units   415

Illustrations – Volume 2

(Figures 1–23 appear in Volume 1)

Frontispiece A1 Pavillion de Breteuil, Bureau International des Poids et Mesures, Sèvres, near Paris

Frontispiece A2 Bushy House, National Physical Laboratory, Teddington

24 – Moles of three chemical elements and three chemical compounds   218

25 – The radian and the steradian   219

26 – A medieval monumental brass of 1483
The Earl of Essex and his wife, Little Easton, Essex   233

27 – Report from *The Times* (29 April 1986) of the Chernobyl incident   252

28 – Title page of Radiological Protection Act 1970   257

29 – Air quality reports on television   264/265

30 – Title page of Decimal Currency Act 1967   291

31 – Title page of Decimal Currency Act 1969   292

32 – The United Kingdom's first decimal coins (1971)   294

33 – Contemporary information for Decimal Day 1971   295

34 – Pages from *The Technical Chemists' Handbook* (Lunge, 1910, Gurney and Jackson)   352/353

35 – The United Kingdom's pre-decimal coins, in piles each weighing approximately one ounce avoirdupois   408

36 – Title page of Weights and Measures Act 1979   419

Appendices

A1   Definitions of the Base Units and Supplementary
      Units of SI   363

A2   Table of SI Prefixes   365

B   Notes on Conversion Tables   366

Conversion Tables

B1   SI and c.g.s. coherent units   367

B2   SI and metric technical units   371

B3   SI and non-coherent metric units   373

B4   SI and British units   378

B5   SI and American units which differ from British units 388

B6   SI and units of radiation   389

B7   Units of pressure   390

C   Units outside the International System   391

D   **Arbitrary scales**

D1   Beaufort Wind Force Scales   395

D2   The Richter Scale for earthquakes   401

D3   Mohs' Scale of Hardness of Minerals   403

D4   The Carat – fineness of gold and a mass unit   404

D5   Examples of dimensionless values   405

E   The United Kingdom's monetary system   407

F   pH Values (measures of acidity/alkalinity/neutrality) 411

G   The Doppler effect and the measurement of speed   412

H   Dimensional analysis   413

J   Disciplines, techniques of measuring and limitations
          resultant on measurements   415

General Acknowledgements

The Author's and Editor's sincere thanks are due to the following:

The Directors of the Bureau International des Poids et Mesures, Sèvres, for supplying photographs from which Frontispiece A1 was re-drawn.

The National Physical Laboratory Teddington for permission to use the illustration for Frontispiece A2 and the end-plate (an NPL photograph © Crown Copyright 1993: reproduced by permission of the Controller of HMSO).

The HMSO Copyright Unit for permission to reproduce the Figures 28, 30, 31 and 36, which are Crown Copyright.

Mr Eric Robson who drew Frontispiece A1 and Figures 24, 32 and 35.

The Times for permission to reproduce Figure 27. The authors of the article were Thomas Prentice and Christopher Mosey.

Teletext Ltd and the British Broadcasting Corporation Ceefax for permission to reproduce pages of their transmissions in Figure 29.

Mr John Puntis for technical proof-reading.

Mrs Gill Vadden and Mrs Suzanne Cunningham for typing and proof-reading.

Thomas McGreevy
Peter Cunningham
June 1996

Author's Personal Acknowledgements

The list of persons who helped me to write these two volumes of *The Basis of Measurement* is rather long as in 1984 my eyesight failed and I became unable to read. My sincere thanks are due to the following friends who participated in this venture, enabling the work to be completed.

Mr Steven Anthony, Mr Ernest Beaumont, Mr Peter Cunningham, Mrs Dorothy May Husselbee, Mrs Alice Elizabeth Theresa Judge, Mrs Hilda Loader, Miss Sheila Saunby and Mrs Margaret Evelyn Tandy.

Special mention must be made of Mrs Stella Winifred Wrigley without whose enthusiasm and continued application the manuscript for the work would not have been completed in my lifetime.

Thomas McGreevy
2 Barnes Way
Bedhampton
Hampshire
PO9 3DU
July 1996

Author's Preface

Lord Kelvin once pointed out that the foundation of science is measurement. Since measurement cannot be made without a system of units, it follows that some knowledge of units is an essential part of education in science and technology.

The influence of science and technology extends to all aspects of everyday life. Members of the general public nowadays may need to know the meaning of new terms such as tog, nit, femto, atomic time and millisievert, as they appear in the newspapers and on the radio and television. Although the subject of units might be regarded as dull, it is in fact surprising how interesting this topic can prove to be.

This work was originally conceived as a single book, but since parts of the publication are likely to appeal to somewhat different readers, it was decided to divide it into two parts, each of which may subsist alone.

The object of Volume 1 is to provide a popular account of the early development of weights and measures, particularly in the Middle East and Western Europe; and also to show how chaotic has been the situation in this field throughout the ages.

Volume 2 deals with the International System of Units (SI). The pervading theme of the work is the hope that this coherent and rational system of units will eventually replace a chaotic situation by an orderly one. With the single exception of the USA, every major country is, in 1996, the user of metric and SI units in commerce and industry.

The author, however, hopes that these two volumes will highlight persisting inconsistencies and sources of errors, so as to lead to their eventual elimination. For example, on the Continent of Europe the comma is used as a decimal marker and this has caused errors to be made in British newspaper reports and in some sectors of commerce. To illustrate this; the figure 37,254 means in the UK and the USA thirty seven thousand two hundred and fifty four. In most European countries the meaning would be thirty seven point two five four.

The above source of error can be avoided by adopting the following practice recommended by the International Standards Organisation (ISO). A space is used instead of a comma to separate groups of 3 digits when dealing with very large numbers. Thus, the UK and USA practice of writing, say, 29,584,238 should be written 29 584 238.

Although it has not been the custom to separate groups of 3 digits **after** the decimal point, it is convenient to use spaces to make easy the reading of the number. An example would appear like this: 2·132 589 04.

In the case of a number with only 4 digits it is permissible, using this convention, to omit the space, thus: 1354 and 9852 and 1000 are examples. This is because the eye can take in 4 digits in a row quite easily but it is difficult to grasp readily a number containing 5 or more digits which are not separated by either commas or spaces.

Thomas McGreevy 1996

Editor's Preface

It was in 1984 that Thomas McGreevy placed a request in the Portsmouth Polytechnic News asking for a measure of help from a fellow lecturer to complete these volumes. Interest and curiosity urged me to respond: I am glad I did; it has proved an agreeable intellectual adventure. Mine has been very much a subsidiary role; acting as a pair of eyes, consultant on some scientific matters and principally as a copy-editor. It has been my brief to update certain passages, as Tom McGreevy's sight has, these past few years, failed him.

Since I, a sighted person, have that obvious advantage, Tom McGreevy has given me full authority to make such amendments as I have felt desirable. In doing so, I have tried to retain the structure and content of the book as the Author conceived it, and to avoid imposing more than modest changes. The significant additions are indicated as follows.

In view of the original lengths of Chapters V and VII, I decided to divide each into sections. Some updating was considered prudent, particularly in view of events in the 1990s: by good fortune, the October 1995 changes in retail practice were implemented just as the final preparation of copy and disc for transmission to the Printers was in hand. Appendices F, G, H and J were specially written. The selection of the illustrations has been mine: it is hoped that they add a measure of interest to the book.

Tom McGreevy's manuscript included both the solidus and the negative index. Recent practice prefers the latter, though the solidus is likely to be more familiar to general readers: hence it is retained in appropriate usage. When SI units are quoted in the conversion tables, negative indices are employed.

Working on the manuscripts of the two volumes sporadically since 1984, and more particularly over the past three years has been both an educational and stimulating experience.

All reasonable care has been taken to avoid and eliminate errors in both the text and the tables. However, should any material mistakes be noted by readers, the publisher and editor will be grateful to have them brought to their attention.

Peter Cunningham, Southend-on-Sea, October 1996

Chapter V Part 1

The International System of Units (SI)
The Seven Base Units

Introduction

This volume commences at Chapter V, as the first four chapters of the work are published in the companion *The Basis of Measurement Volume 1 Historical Aspects*, by the same Author and Editor. The original intention was to publish the work in one volume, but separate bindings were considered more appropriate. **Whilst each volume may complement the other, each is intended to subsist on its own, and may appeal to different readers**.

Chapter V, which opens this volume, has been divided into three sections. The first considers principally the seven base units of SI; the second, the submultiples and multiples; and the third, codes of practice.

International bodies and their recommendations

As mentioned in Chapter III in the companion volume; at Sèvres on the outskirts of Paris is a parcel of land which is regarded as internationally owned, and not part of The Republic of France. In 1875 this site was given by the French Government to the many nations who were signatory to the Metre Convention.

The buildings on the site form Le Bureau International des Poids et Mesures (BIPM), or The International Bureau of Weights and Measures. Here are kept the etalons or material standards for length and mass which have been used as the base units in the metric system. Much research and development in the fields of measurement is carried out here; and naturally, close co-operation is maintained with such bodies as the United States National Bureau of Standards (NBS) and The National Physical Laboratory (NPL) in the United Kingdom.

The body with overall responsibility, since 1875, for all international matters concerning the metric system is La Conférence Générale des Poids et Mesures (CGPM), or in English, The General Conference on Weights and Measures. Its membership is drawn from more than 40 nations. Originally convening at irregular intervals, it now meets every four years. Between these meetings, there is a standing body – Le Comité International des Poids et Mesures (CIPM), or The International Committee on Weights and Measures. Its work and recommendations need to be ratified by the CGPM.

Two international organisations do allied work on standards, and electrical matters. These are respectively, The International Organisation for Standardisation (ISO), and The International Electrotechnical Commission (IEC). These august bodies all recommend for universal use Le Système International d'Unités, that is The International System of Units; the abbreviation SI having been adopted to denote this in all languages. This abbreviation SI implies inclusion of the definite article and should be rendered 'SI', not 'The SI'.

The seven base units of SI

The International System of Units is essentially an expansion of the MKSA (metre, kilogram, second, ampere) system. The latter was devised for use mainly for those branches of applied science dealing with engineering and allied topics. By introducing three more base units the system can be used for all branches of science and technology. The seven base units are given in Table XI.

Table XI

The seven SI base units

nature of quantity	unit	symbol
length	metre	m
mass	kilogram	kg
time interval	second	s
electric current	ampere	A
temperature interval	kelvin	K
power of light source	candela	cd
amount of substance	mole	mol

[In addition to these, two supplementary units are recognised; the unit of plane angle, the radian; and the unit of solid angle, the steradian]

This chapter now continues with discussion on measurements with particular consideration of the seven base units of SI, and the principle units derived from such measurements, together with information on prefixes, and a gradually developing code of practice.

Length

The increased precision with which the verification of the velocity of light in a vacuum has developed resulted in a new definition of the metre being formulated. In brief, the new definition affirms that the metre is the distance travelled by light in 0·000 000 003 335 640 952 second of time in a vacuum. The official definition is given in Appendix A1.

In 1960 the definition of the metre based on a material standard was superseded by one based on the wavelength of a certain radiation emitted by excited krypton–86. The earlier definition could not allow the standard to be realised to better than about 4 parts in 10^9. The new definition opened the way to a higher degree of precision due to the development of the laser, and frequency-measuring techniques. In effect the new definition had resulted in a fixed value being given to the speed of light, namely 299 792 458 m s^{-1} exactly in a vacuum.

It is convenient here to consider three units that are simple integer powers of the metre, namely the square metre, m^2; the cubic metre, m^3; and the dioptre, m^{-1}.

Area

In any rational system of measurement, unit area is defined as the area of a square whose length of side is 1 unit of length. Thus, unit area in SI is that of a square with length of side 1 metre and is called 1 square metre (abbreviation 1 m^2). Although the above statement seems trivial or superfluous, it is in fact, not the only possibility. It would be feasible to use the circle instead of the square as the shape used when defining unit area. This was actually done in the USA by electrical engineers when specifying the cross-sectional area of electrical conductors used in cables. The unit of length chosen for this purpose was 1 mil, equal to 0·001 inch, called a 'thou' in Great Britain. Unit area, called 1 circular mil, is the area of a circle of diameter 1 mil. From this it follows that the area A of any circle of diameter d mils is $A = d^2$ circular mils. The advantages of this simple relationship for this restricted application are clear.

If, for example, a conductor of circular cross-section is required to have an area of, say, 10 000 circular mils, then the required diameter of the conductor is $\sqrt{10\,000}$ = 100 mils = 0·1 inch. It is only when a move is made to apply this system to areas of other than circular contour that the lack of rationality becomes clear. The area of a square with side of length L mils would be $A = (4/\pi)L^2$. In a similar manner the constants $2/\pi$ and $4/\pi$ would appear in all sorts of formulae for areas which do not relate to circular geometry. The traditional system of defining unit area based on a square contour is thus seen to be soundly based; the constant π then appears in formulae relating to area where it is logical to expect it, as in the case of the circle and the ellipse. The smallest unit of area at present in use is the barn, equal to 10^{-28} m^2, and used to express areas in the disciplines of nuclear science.

Although the prefix deca- is not a 'preferred' multiple, it has been used extensively under another name to specify areas in metric countries. The 'are', pronounced so as to rhyme with 'fair', is equal to the square decametre; 1 $(dam)^2 = 100$ m^2. Of greater use, however, is the hecto-are, abbreviated to hectare, symbol ha, which is equal to 100 are = 10^4 m^2; or equal to the square hectometre (100 m × 100 m). This unit will replace the British unit, the acre, for land surveys and similar applications. One hectare equals 2·471 05 acres.

Volume

Unit volume in SI, 1 cubic metre (m^3), is not of a particularly convenient order of magnitude for many applications. In Germany and Austria this unit is called the 'Festmeter' when used to denote volume of timber, and other applications.

The word 'capacity' is often used to denote a unit of volume intended for use in commerce for liquids and for a restricted range of solids such as grain. The unit of capacity in widespread use in metric countries is the litre, once called the 'pinte' and later the 'kanne'; although 'litron' was in vogue even before the advent of the metric system. This unit has an unusual history. It was at first defined as one cubic decimetre. There was no etalon or material standard for this unit, and the difficulty in realising such an artifact in practical construction with the same degrees of accuracy as the metre bar led to a change in the definition.

Between 1901 and 1964 the litre was defined as the volume occupied by a mass of 1 kilogramme of pure water at its temperature of maximum density (4°C), since this seemed to make for coherence. It was only when methods of measurement became highly refined that it was realised that there could be incompatibility between the objective and its realisation. In the c.g.s. (rarely cgs, C. G. S. or CGS) – centimetre, gram, second – system it had originally been the intention to make compatible three base units:

unit volume	1 cm^3
unit mass	1 gram
unit density for water	1 kg/dm^3 (but called 1 kg/litre).

Having regard to the relatively crude measuring techniques available in 1901, the proposals had the merit of simplicity. When, however, measurements could be made accurately to within a few parts in a million, it became evident that incompatibility existed between the two parameters of volume and density for a single substance. Retaining the mass and density relationships, one litre was found [by Charles Guillaume] to measure $1.000\ 028\ dm^3$. If, however, the cubic decimetre is required to be exactly equal to the defined capacity of 1 litre, then the density of water becomes $0.999\ 972\ kg/litre$. The latter course was adopted by the CGPM in 1964, since the identity 1 litre = 1 cubic decimetre is the more important relationship from the point of view of practical applications. Although the 1901 definition of the litre was altered in this way, a rider was added to the 1964 decision to the effect that for measurements of very great precision the name cubic decimetre should be used to avoid any possible confusion with the pre-1964 litre. Since the difference between these two values amounts to 1 part in 36 000 it has been suggested as a rough guide that where the precision in measurement in a practical case exceeds 1 part in 20 000, the words 'cubic decimetre' should be used instead of the word 'litre'.

Since 1 cubic metre is equal to 1000 litres, and that in the case of water this has a mass of 1000 kg or 1 tonne, it makes the necessary calculations easy. This is particularly useful, since concentration is now often specified in grams per litre.

The cubic centimetre finds wide application in physics, chemistry and the applied sciences; and is likely to continue in use. The gap between the base unit $1\ m^3$ and the next lower 'preferred' unit $1\ mm^3$ is in the ratio 10^9 to 1, and hence intermediate units are necessary in practice. Formerly the cubic centimetre carried the abbreviation cc and even ccm, but these notations are now obsolete. On the other hand the abbreviation cm^3 is not favoured in some metric countries, particularly when handwritten, as by doctors and pharmacists; the superscript 3 might be mistaken for a number relating to the next word or quantity if it appears on a prescription form. It is almost universal practice in France to use millilitre for cubic centimetre, writing mL instead of cm^3.

On the Continent of Europe, the derived SI unit 1 cubic metre was known as the 'stere' when applied to a large volume of firewood. The unit became obsolete when firewood came to be sold by weight towards the end of the 19th century.

The dioptre

This unit is mentioned here merely because it fits in neatly into the schema. The power of a lens may be measured in dioptres. The dioptre is defined as the reciprocal of the principle focal length in metres. It was adopted in 1875 at Le Congrès International des Sciences Médicales held in Brussels, though the dioptre has never become adopted as an SI derived unit. Nonetheless it finds wide use and recognition by opticians.

A converging lens of principle focal length 1 metre has a power of 1×1^{-1} dioptres (= 1 dioptre). A similar lens but of focal length $\frac{1}{2}$ metre has a power of $1 \times \frac{1}{2}^{-1}$ dioptres (= 2 dioptres).

Diverging lenses are ascribed negative values. Thus a spectacle lens for a short-sighted person may be of focal length 0·4 metre. Its power in dioptres is therefore $-1 \times 0\cdot4^{-1}$ dioptres (= $-2\cdot5$ dioptres).

Mass

The mass of an object is that property directly related to its inertia, ie its tendency to remain at rest or to maintain uniform motion in a straight line, unless acted upon by a force which compels a change.

Although in the case of length, the former material standard has been superseded by a natural standard, this type of development has not yet (1996) taken place in the case of the metric unit of mass. In principle it would be possible to use the mass of an atom of a particular kind as a scientific standard of mass, but techniques have not yet been developed to produce a standard more accurate than that obtained by 'weighing' in the principal standards laboratories of the world, where a difference equal to about 1 ounce in 30 000 tons can be detected. That is 28 grams in 30 000 tonnes.

Unit mass in SI is the kilogram. The international prototype kilogram takes the form of a cylinder of alloy composed of 90 per cent platinum and 10 per cent iridium, of height equal to its diameter. This piece of metal is kept at Sèvres near Paris, but copies (some of platinum-iridium and some of stainless steel) are held in the various countries that were signatory to the Metre Convention of 1875. These copies are returned to Sèvres as occasion demands for comparison with the prototype; this verification can be done to an accuracy of about 1 part in 10^9.

In the 1990s it has been found that even minute concentrations of mercury vapour in the air leads inevitably to contamination and perceptible increases in the masses of these kilogram standards.[167]

Force, work and power

From the base units of length and mass we derive the SI unit of force. Unit force 1 newton (symbol N) gives to a mass of 1 kilogram an acceleration of 1 metre per second every second. When a force of 1 newton is exerted through a distance of 1 metre, the work done or energy expended is 1 joule (symbol J).

The rate at which energy is expended is called 'power'. Unit power in SI is the watt (symbol W), equal to the rate of expenditure of energy equal to 1 joule per second.

Originally the joule and the watt were purely electrical units. In SI they can be used to quantify all kinds of energy and power; electrical, mechanical, chemical etc. A good example of this is the practice of rating the power of motor car engines in kilowatts. The horse-power must be abandoned as the Continental horse-power equals 735·75 watts though the UK horse-power is equal to 746 watts.

Time intervals and the calendar

It is a great advantage that in all the various systems of units used in science, technology and commerce, that the base unit of time is the same, namely one second. The regrettable feature of time measurements, however, is the fact that the multiples of the base unit of time, one second, are not decimal multiples or powers of 10. If instead of 60 seconds in one minute we had 100, and 100 minutes in one hour, calculations involving periods of time longer than one second would be simplified.

An attempt to do this was made in France by a decree of 24 November 1793, when the ferment for change after the Revolution still prevailed, and it was felt desirable to eradicate associations with the Gregorian Calendar. The new annual pattern was one that had been used in ancient Egypt: 13 sub-divisions consisting of 12×30 days and 1×5 (or 6) days. Inscriptions of the reign of Pepi II (c 2500 BC) show that the Egyptians were in the habit of adding five days each year to their year of 360 days. Such a calendar pattern, having its origins directly from Egyptian pre-history, is still extant and used in Ethiopia today. That country, in 1995, advertises its '13 months of sunshine' – the Tourist Board motto – *inter alia* by means of its postal franking.

In Revolutionary France, each year was to begin on 22 September, on which day the Republic had been proclaimed in 1792 – and it was also the day of the autumnal equinox. The 'Republican' year was to be divided into 12 parts, but these 'months' each consisted of 3 'decads' of 10 days each. To these 360 days were added 5 extra ones at the end of each year, or 6 in each leap year.

From there the similarity with the 'Egyptian' pattern ends. Each day of the Republic of France was divided into 10 hours, and each hour into 100 'minutes', each of 100 'seconds'. A detailed account of this odd phase in the history of time-keeping is given by Kennelly[188] who attributed its failure mainly to lack of international support. This division of the day into 100 000 parts was abandoned in 1795 and the whole scheme was dropped in favour of the current (Gregorian) calendar in 1806.

An attempt was made in 1900 at Le Congrès International de Chronomètre to introduce a unit of time, to be called the cé, equal to one hundredth of a day. Proposed sub-divisions were the decicé (one tenth of a cé) and the millicé (one thousandth of a cé). This again proved an abortive attempt to decimalise the day. The use of 60 seconds and 60 minutes is so completely accepted now that there is no possibility of introducing a hectosecond, a kilosecond, nor a megasecond in everyday life. This consolidates in SI units the only important feature which is non-coherent; it does the same, of course, for the related derived unit systems. On the other hand the sub-multiples of the second in decimal form are very widely used, particularly the millisecond (10^{-3} s), the microsecond (10^{-6} s) and the nanosecond (10^{-9} s).

Advances in the science of measurement of time have brought about changes in the basis upon which the unit of time is determined. It was natural that the early bases for the measurement of time should have been based upon the rotation of the earth on its axis. By observation of star transits, the mean solar day was divided into 86 400 parts ($60 \times 60 \times 24 = 86\,400$) giving the unit of time 1 second, called Universal Time or Mean Solar Time, and designated by the symbol UTO. Subsequent observations showed that a small correction was needed to allow for a small movement of the earth's pole, and the corrected value was known as UT1. If a further correction is applied because of the seasonal variation of the speed of rotation of the earth and other variables (not excluding weather conditions) the resultant unit of time was called UT2.

The quartz clock and the atomic clock

It was the development of the 'quartz clock' which enabled astronomical observations to be averaged over periods of a year or more, thus detecting the small variations mentioned above in the rate of rotation of the earth. This new technique followed from the development of quartz oscillators for use in radio-transmission systems. The development of the first quartz crystal clock is attributed to two American inventors, J W Horton and W A Morrison, in 1928. It is based on the piezo-electric effect which occurs in a range of materials, and particularly a massive single crystal of silica (silicon dioxide) called quartz. If a slab of this material is cut from a crystal so that the sides of the slab make certain angles with the electric axes of the crystal, the application of a potential difference across the faces of the slab produces changes in the dimensions of the material.

Conversely; if by pressure, the dimensions of the crystal are changed, a potential difference appears between the faces of the slab. When such a crystal is set into oscillation at a suitable frequency by an alternating potential difference applied to it, the electrical frequency locks onto the natural frequency of the crystal which is a parameter determined by its elastic properties. This frequency remains very stable, and crystal-controlled oscillators have been used extensively in radio-communication circuits where great stability is important. This principle is utilised for time measurement by the combination of a quartz oscillator and an integrating mechanism which counts the number of oscillations; and then transforms this number into seconds, minutes and hours. The complete equipment then forms a 'quartz clock'.

Originally the quartz clock was developed for the purpose of giving a shorter interval of time than the pendulum or the tuning fork in order to facilitate the measurement of radio-frequencies. It was soon found that these clocks were vastly superior timepieces to anything that had previously been developed, and actually give a more uniform performance than the earth, which by its rotation was itself regarded as a time standard. If a perfect clock had been available from the year 1900, it would at the end of 1994 show that the earth in its rotation would be about 2·5 minutes behind schedule. This brings out another advantage of the quartz clock as a time standard. Astronomical standards of time require averaging out over very long periods of time and can only be corrected retrospectively; quartz clocks enable accurate measurement to be available much more quickly and can be corrected where necessary in a relatively short time. Although Universal Time is quite accurate enough for such purposes as marine navigation, the small errors revealed by the quartz clock on the basis of UT led to the introduction of a more satisfactory unit called Ephemeris Time (ET).

Astronomers have found that the period of revolution of the earth around the sun is more nearly constant than the period of the earth's axial rotation, and this fact was made the basis for the development of Ephemeris Time. The unit known as the second of ET has been defined in such a way that it represents virtually the average value of UT over more than 100 years. The definition of the second of ET adopted in 1956 was abrogated by CGPM in 1967. An atomic resonator used in conjunction with a quartz oscillator is called an atomic clock.

The basic principle upon which the atomic clock (developed c.1948) is operated is the fact that the frequency of the radiation absorbed or emitted when an electron in an atom or molecule changes from one excitation state to another has a constant value which can be calculated for a given case. Of the few possible spectral lines constituting a potential standard of frequency and hence time interval, the one resulting from transitions between two ground state levels of certain electrons of the caesium–133 atom has proved very suitable for this purpose. The frequency of just over 9 GHz is a convenient one for laboratory purposes. The atomic resonator developed at the NPL by L Essen opened up a new era in the matter of precision time and frequency measurement. This gives rise to the definition of the second of atomic time, known officially as International Atomic Time and called TAI, from the sequence of words of the French rendition. The definition is given in full in Appendix A1.

There is widespread application for signals based on Coordinated Universal Time, known at UTC (from the French sequence of the words). For marine navigation the general need is to have UTC to within about 0·1 second. Similarly other applications relating to the earth's rotation, even though this be irregular, need time signals related to Universal Time, this being the time scale which governs our daily lives; it was more formally known as Greenwich Mean Time (GMT). Thus whereas astronomical time gives us the time of day, the atomic clock provides us with an extremely accurate and convenient measure of time interval.

The time signals sent out by the BBC have the following features. From 1 January 1972 the time signal consists of 5 short pips followed by a lengthened sixth pip or 'beep'. The exact time is indicated by the beginning of the beep. This elongated pip is important in two ways. It identifies without ambiguity the particular pip, the beginning of which gives UTC exactly. In addition it enables 7 pips to be broadcast occasionally without loss of identification. The additional increment is called a 'leap second'. This insertion of an extra second about once every two years brings together Atomic Time and UTC, which would otherwise gradually diverge to an unacceptable extent if left uncorrected for several years.

Time and frequency

There is a very close link between the general idea of time and the idea of frequency. Let a regular recurring phenomenon repeat its pattern of variations f times every second: ergo, we introduce the idea of frequency. This value f is called the hertz, symbol Hz. The duration of a single pattern of variation is called the periodic time, denoted by T, and its numerical value is $T = 1/f$ second. The importance of this simple relationship lies in the fact that the physical quantity in science which can be measured to a higher degree of accuracy than any other, is frequency. From this it follows that time intervals can be measured with such extreme accuracy that the base unit of time is the one most accurately specified and reproduced. Moreover it has the unique property of being universally available as a standard for reference purposes, by means of radio-transmission of appropriate signals.

Readers should note that the derived SI unit of rotational frequency is s^{-1}, that is the reciprocal of time. An electric motor may be said to run at, say, 30 rotations per second: not be it noted, 30 hertz.

Electric current

When the MKSA system of units was being developed it was essential to produce a definition of unit current that would result in a value identical with unit current in the c.g.s. system.

The c.g.s. definition of unit electric current was based on a highly artificial concept involving the force experienced by a hypothetical single unit magnetic pole situated in the magnetic field of a current-carrying conductor. The definition gave an 'absolute ampere' and the unit for use in practice was one-tenth of this value. The MKSA definition of unit current gives the same result for the magnitude of the ampere, avoiding the introduction of the hypothetical unit magnetic pole. This definition applies without any change to unit current in SI and is given in Appendix A1.

Temperature interval and temperature scales

When ideas and units in thermodynamics were first being formulated, the transformation of heat energy into mechanical energy (and *vice versa*) was not known, not appreciated, or not taken into account; and the various units were devised without regard to energy consideration. This fact reveals one of the big differences in concept between the traditional heat units and the single energy unit, the joule, which is such an important feature of SI.

In the c.g.s. system of units, those relating to heat were rather neatly fitted into the general unit system. Unit volume of water (1 cubic centimetre) was the base unit of mass (1 gram); and the process of raising the temperature of this mass through one degree on the centigrade scale (now called the Celsius scale) resulted in the realisation of the unit of heat (1 calorie); this also made the specific heat of water equal to unity.

Differences in the methods and specification of measurement of heat units revealed differences in the magnitude of the unit, which became significant. There were at one time fifteen different units of heat bearing the name 'calorie'; and of these, five have been used until quite recently. In terms of the SI energy unit, the joule, these five 'calorie' heat units have values as shown in Table XII.

The current agreed practical value of the Btu (where Btu means British thermal unit) is based on the indirect definition $1 \cdot 8$ Btu/lb $= 1$ kcal/kg where the calorie is $4 \cdot 1868$ J exactly. The latter figure represents a very slight adjustment of the original IT calorie, to make the digits divisible by nine, which facilitates conversions of units determined by the ratio 5/9. [As required when converting degrees Fahrenheit into degrees Celsius].

It is important to dispense with the Fahrenheit scale of temperature and its associated Rankine scale as soon as possible. The magnitude of the temperature interval in both cases is the same, but on the Fahrenheit scale the freezing point of water is 32°F and the boiling point 212°F. The $212 - 32 = 180$ intervals of temperature correspond to the 100 intervals of temperature on the Celsius scale, and hence

Table XII	
Equivalent values of various calorie units in joules	
thermochemical calorie	4·1840 J
15° calorie	4·1855 J
international steam table calorie (IT)	4·1868 J
mean 0° to 100° calorie	4·1897 J
4° calorie	4·2045 J

each interval on the Fahrenheit scale is 100/180 = 5/9 of the temperature interval on the Celsius scale. Any mark or value on the Fahrenheit scale, say F, is related to the mark, say C, on the Celsius scale for the temperature by the relationship F = (9/5)C + 32.

The Rankine scale starts at the absolute zero of all absolute scales of temperature, and is numerically 459·67 degrees greater than the corresponding value on the Fahrenheit scale. This scale has been used mainly by engineers when using imperial units.

It is likewise desirable to eliminate the Réaumur scale of temperature (introduced in 1731) which has had limited use, mainly in Germany, Russia and Spain; in recent years it has persisted in the USA in the brewing and sugar refining industries. The Réaumur scale freezing point of water is the zero point, and the boiling point of water at atmospheric pressure is marked 80° on that scale.

All scientific work is done in terms of either the Celsius scale (for 'customary' temperature) or in terms of the Kelvin scale of absolute temperature. The temperature interval is the same for both scales and is called the kelvin, symbol K. In 1967 the CGPM set up the kelvin as the SI unit of temperature interval, using the words as in Appendix A1. This definition uses the 'triple point of water' by which is meant the temperature and pressure at which ice, water and water vapour coexist in equilibrium.

It was Lord Kelvin (1824–1907) who had introduced the concept of a 'Thermodynamic Scale' of temperature. According to this idea, equal increments of temperature are defined as the intervals between which a perfect heat engine working on the Carnot cycle would perform equal amounts of work. This definition has the advantage of being independent of the physical properties of any substance engaged for use in realising the unit. This scale can be shown to be identical with the 'perfect gas scale'. The latter is based on the relationship which would exist for a perfect gas, pV = kT under all conditions. Measurement of the pressure p at a constant value of volume V (or of V at constant p) would give the value of the absolute temperature T since the value of the constant k is known from theoretical considerations. This provides a means of solving the problem of realising the unit of thermodynamic temperature, which is very fortunate since it is not a practical proposition to do this from the definition involving a perfect heat engine working on the Carnot cycle. Although the word 'scale' has been used in the preceding paragraphs as has been customary in many textbooks, it should be borne in mind that the real objective has been the setting up of the base unit of temperature interval.

In 1927 there was set up by the CGPM a 'practical' scale of temperature, accurately reproducible, and as near as possible to the thermodynamic scale within the limits of the then-known experimental techniques; this scale was called the 'International Temperature Scale'. It was first revised in 1948 by the 9th CGPM when it was decided that the zero of the centesimal scale should be defined as the temperature 0·0100 degree below that of the triple point of water. Three possible names were considered to denote the degree on this scale. These were (a) degree centigrade, (b) centesimal degree, and (c) degree Celsius. The last of these was decided on and the word 'Celsius' was adopted for what has hitherto been known as 'centigrade' scale.

Andere Celsius (1701–1744) was a Swedish astronomer and he proposed this particular type of scale of temperature in 1742. Actually the scale used by Celsius had zero for the boiling point of water and 100° for the melting point of ice. Celsius probably used thermometers devised by his compatriot Palmburg whose scale of temperature ran from zero, representing the coldest day of the year, to 100 representing the hottest day. In devising his scale with 100 representing a low point, Celsius may have contrived to distance his scale from Palmburg's efforts. The designation of the fixed points of Celsius were invented in 1743 by J P Christen.[144B] The name Celsius had the advantage of eliminating any possible confusion with the centi-grade, that is one hundredth of the unit of angle known as the grade which was used in some European countries. In this system of measurement of angle the right angle is divided into 100 equal parts or 'grades'.

Further revision of the international scale of temperature took place in 1960 when the scale was designated the International Practical Scale of Temperature (IPST). The zero value 'fixed point' on the Celsius scale was formerly realised by the choice of the melting point of pure crushed ice. An improvement in the location of the zero point was made by a change from the ice point to the triple point of water, ie the point at which solid, liquid and vapour co-exist in equilibrium. This decision of the 10th CGPM in 1954 was made because the triple point of water is reproducible to a higher degree of accuracy than the ice point; the temperature interval between the triple point and the boiling point of pure water at standard atmospheric pressure can be measured to within 1 part in 10^5. The interval between the ice point and the triple point is 0·01 K. The definition of the triple point as 273·16 on the thermodynamic scale fixes the zero of the Celsius scale as 273·15 on the thermodynamic scale.

The 13th CGPM in 1968 decided on the name 'kelvin' and the symbol 'K' for the unit of thermodynamic temperature. This paved the way for the abolition of the former styles of nomenclature such as 'degree Kelvin', 'deg', and °K; which should now be shunned. The unit of temperature interval must be called the kelvin, not the 'degree kelvin' and the symbol is just 'K' by itself. For example, when working in terms of the Celsius scale, a temperature rise from 15°C to 70°C should be written 70°C–15°C = (70–15)K = 55K. Likewise on the absolute scale one would have, for example, 390K – 280K = 110K. The elimination of the abbreviation 'deg' is a distinct advantage, since in addition to avoiding confusion in the English language, it removes a symbol which has no meaning in some other languages. In Sweden a temperature interval has been called a 'grad', which again is a possible source of confusion with the word for a unit of angle in some Continental countries. The International Practical Scale of Temperature is subject to continuous improvement in its representation of the thermodynamic scale.

The basis of measurement of temperature for many years relied on the expansion/contraction of liquids: the mercury- or ethanol-in-glass thermometer. Electronic devices that monitor the subtle changes in

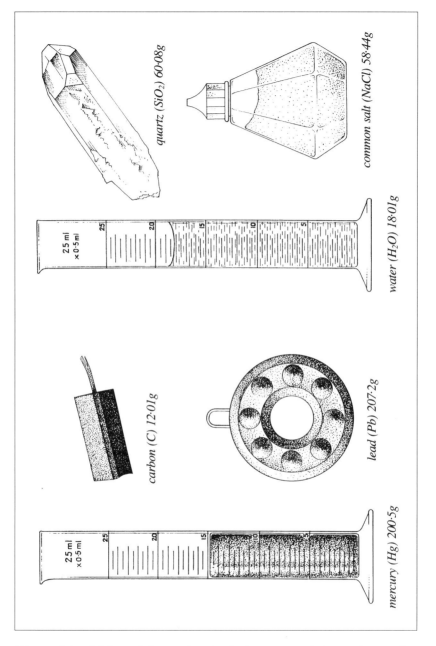

Figure 24 – Moles of three chemical elements and three chemical
   compounds.

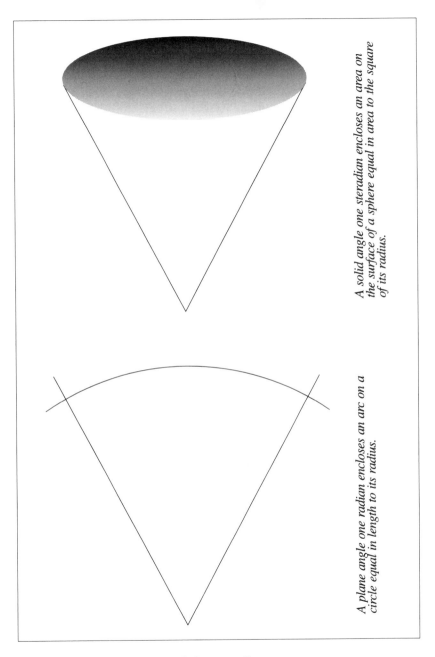

A solid angle one steradian encloses an area on the surface of a sphere equal in area to the square of its radius.

A plane angle one radian encloses an arc on a circle equal in length to its radius.

Figure 25 – The radian and the steradian.

electrical resistance accompanying temperature changes, eg thermisters and reverse-biased diodes, are now increasingly common: most refined are those giving rise to the so-called platinum resistance scale. For work of low accuracy, liquid-crystal thermometers have some applications.

Luminous intensity

The unit candlepower or international candle was used for many years to denote the power of a light source. None of the etalons set up for this purpose were candles. After the use of various types of oil lamps there followed electric filament lamps to represent the base units of luminous intensity. But reproducibility was always a problem. About 1960 the US candle was specified as a particular fraction of the average horizontal candlepower of 45 carbon filament lamps preserved at the Bureau of Standards. There was a big difference between the degree of precision with which the power of a light source could be ascertained and the degree of precision with which the other base units in SI could be measured. An attempt to close this gap was made by the CGPM when flames and similar light sources were replaced by the use of the surface of molten platinum at its melting point (1768°C). This too proved to be unsatisfactory.

In October 1979 the 16th meeting of the CGPM pointed out that radio-metric techniques had been developed to a stage where a new definition of a primary light source could be made with a satisfactory degree of precision. The name candela (symbol cd) was given to the new unit. The definition specified is given in Appendix A1.

Amount of substance

Long consideration was given to the adoption of a seventh base unit in SI, called by chemists the 'amount of substance'. This is not the same as the mass of a substance, although each is a quantity independent of pressure and temperature. In the case of a particular element or compound the amount of substance is directly proportional to its mass; however, the 'mass' and 'amount of substance' have different meanings.

The c.g.s. unit of amount of substance was the mole, symbol 'mol'. It was based on the number of atoms, in what was formerly called 'one gramme atom', of carbon–12. The current estimate of this number is $6·022\ 1367 \times 10^{23}$. At the 14th CGPM in 1971 it was decided that the mole should be the seventh base unit of the International System. The definition of this unit is given in Appendix A1. Since 1960 the isotopic mass scale has been based on the value of 12 exactly for carbon–12 and hence its use in the definition of the mole. It will be noticed that in the case of amount of substance, the existing c.g.s. unit has been adopted; the only change is in the wording of the definition which naturally is based on the kilogram. Figure 24 illustrates moles of some common elements and compounds.

In derived units the word 'molar' denotes 'divided by amount of substance'. Thus molar mass is in terms of kg/mol, molar volume in m^3/mol, molar internal energy in J/mol, molar heat capacity in J/mol K and molar entropy in J/mol K. Other derived units are molality, in mol/kg; and molarity or concentration which is expressed in mol/m^3. In the UK, blood sugar concentration is usually expressed as millimoles per litre (mmol/L) instead of mg/dL as previously used; and as is still used in many parts of the world: 18 mg/dL = 1 mmol/L [since the relative molecular mass of glucose $C_6H_{12}O_6$ is 180 – Ed].

Chapter V Part 2

Prefixes and Suffixes for SI Units

Prefixes as applied in the International System of Units

The great breadth of science, in its study of the very large (as in astronomy) and of the very small (as in nucleonics) means that whatever system of units is chosen, some or all of the base units are bound to prove inconveniently large or far too small for some practical purposes. The system of prefixes devised for use in SI to denote multiples and submultiples of the base units is a great boon, and enables a very wide range of numerical values to be dealt with conveniently. A list of these prefixes is given later in this section, together with examples to illustrate their use.

Most people will be familiar with prefixes such as kilo-, centi-, and milli-; which have been in use since the turn of the 20th century. The development of the present complete system of prefixes and their related symbols did not, however, take place in an entirely systematic manner. The list of symbols adopted in 1879 by the CIPM included:

km and kg [k = kilo]	ha and hl [h = hecto]
s [= stère = cubic metre]	cm cl and cg [c = centi]
mm and mg [m = milli]	dal [= decalitre]
dm dl and dg [d = deci]	t [= metric tonne]
μ [= micrometre]	q [= quintal metrique = 100 kilograms].

It was 22 years later that the symbols ml for millilitre and λ for microlitre were added. A suggestion was also discussed at that time that capital letters should be used in the symbols for multiples (say, D for deca) and small letters for submultiples (say, d for deci). However this idea was not adopted. In 1908 certain additional symbols were recommended by the CIPM, resulting in the following complete list of symbols for prefixes:

M for myria 10^4	d for deci 10^{-1}
k for kilo 10^3	c for centi 10^{-2}
h for hecto 10^2	m for milli 10^{-3}
da for deca 10^1	

Here we see emerging the clear idea of a prefix suitable for application for any base unit. Up to this point, the prefixes designated for multiples had Greek roots, and those for submultiples had Latin roots. The previously accepted symbols were thus:

μ for 10^{-6} metre λ for 10^{-6} litre γ for 1^{-6} gramme

These were clearly not prefixes in the newly-emerging sense of the word. From about the year 1900 physicists brought into use the Greek letter μ as a symbol for a prefix so that:

micrometre changed from μ to μm
microgramme changed from γ to μg
microlitre changed from λ to μl (or μL).

It was, however, only in 1935 that the CIPM adopted officially the symbol μ for the new prefix 'micro' denoting 10^{-6}. At the same time this Committee abolished altogether the prefix 'myria' and allotted its symbol M to the new prefix 'mega' denoting 10^6 since this prefix had come into extensive use in electrical science. The proposal to have capital letters for all symbols denoting multiples was again put forward but not adopted. The restriction of prefixes derived from the Greek to multiples had been broken by the introduction of 'micro'. Thus when extra prefixes were introduced subsequently, no notice was taken of the earlier intention to have Greek derivatives for multiples, and Latin ones for submultiples. The Second World War (1939–1945) caused delay to the further development of the system of prefixes, and the extended range of values under consideration in 1940 did not come into use officially until 1948 when the International Union of Pure and Applied Physics (IUPAP) approved the following additional prefixes and their symbols:

T for tera 10^{12}	n for nano 10^{-9}
G for giga 10^9	p for pico 10^{-12}

These prefixes were finally approved by the CIPM in 1960. In the same year the IUPAP added two more symbols and prefixes:

f for femto 10^{-15} a for atto 10^{-18}

These were adopted by the CGPM in 1964. The spelling of 'tera' should be noted since there has been introduced into engineering vocabulary a prefix 'tero'. This derives from the Greek root denoting 'take care of', and terotechnology is a recently-coined word for maintenance engineering.

In 1974 the CIPM recommended to the CGPM the adoption of the following extra prefixes: peta, symbol P for 10^{15}; and exa, symbol E for 10^{18}. Final ratification was agreed in 1975.

The 19th meeting of the CGPM in October 1991 ratified the introduction of four extra prefixes; namely, zetta for 10^{21}, yotta 10^{24}, zepto for 10^{-21} and yocto for 10^{-24}. The CIPM stated that the derivation of these prefixes was as follows: the names zepto and zetta are derived from septo, suggesting the number seven (the seventh power of 10^3) and the letter z is substituted for the letter s to avoid the duplicate use of the letter s as a symbol. The names yocto and yotta are derived from octo, suggesting the number eight (the eighth power of 10^3) and the y is added to avoid the use of the letter o as a symbol because it may be confused with the character zero.

SI prefixes for multiples of a base unit

Although it was once proposed that the prefixes recommended for general use should rise in multiples of thousands, some of the prefixes for multiples less than one thousand have been found to be very convenient in certain applications.

deca (deka), (Greek, ten), 10^1, symbol da

This is a non-preferred multiple, and has not been in use at all in some metric countries. In general it is hardly worthwhile introducing a separate prefix for 10 times the base unit or 10 times any derived unit. The following are some examples where this prefix has found an application. In the planning of illumination schemes, use has sometimes been made of the decalumen. The planet Jupiter is reported to be a strong source of emission of electromagnetic waves in the decametre range.

hecto, (Greek, hundred), 10^2, symbol h

This is also a non-preferred multiple, and hence its extension beyond the present common usage should not be encouraged. However, in the measurement of land area, the hecto-are, contracted to hectare, happens to be a very suitable unit for very many practical purposes; 1 hectare = 100 are = 100 × 100 square metres. The FAO publishes statistics each year which include, amongst other items, the area of the major vineyards in the world in millions of hectares, together with the production therefrom of wine in millions of hectolitres. (One hectolitre equals 22 imperial gallons). The Food and Agricultural Organisation is an Agency of the United Nations.

Engineers, for some applications, are using as a unit of pressure or stress the hectobar; 1 hbar = 100 bar = 10^7 Pa.

kilo, a term adopted by the French to denote '1000 times', or 10^3, symbol k

A span of 1000 metres is a very convenient quantity for distance measurements on earth; and hence the kilometre, symbol km, will replace the various units such as the mile, of which there are at least three different values in current use (1996).

There has developed in some sections of industry the practice of using the abbreviation K by itself to denote thousands of some units commonly used in that industry. For example, in electronics a resistor of resistance 15 000 ohms might be referred to, both in speech and in writing, as a 15K resistor. Amongst computer users reference might be made to kilobits or to kilobytes. Although in one sense the use of

K might seem more logical than the use of k since most of the other prefixes which are multiples are symbolised by capitals, nevertheless the practice of using K by itself in the above manner to denote thousands is a localised one and should be discouraged.

In computer science a thousand is an inconvenient number, being to the base ten; hence K is taken to stand for that integer power of two which is closest to 1000, which is 1024. This is very convenient in the binary (base 2) numbers, being 2^{10} or two to the power of ten. A byte is a group of eight binary digits called bits, for short – where each bit can be 'on' or 'off', ie a 1 or a 0. With eight bits it is possible to have 256 decimal numbers from 0 to 255. Random access memory or RAM is measured in kilobytes (K) of information or data. A RAM of 64K is 1024 multiplied by 64; equals 65 536 bytes of RAM.

Some further illustrations of the prefix kilo

In connection with the sale of herrings on the wholesale markets, the traditional quantity called the cran has been replaced by the 'unit' equal to 100 kilograms.

With the need to conserve energy, in Japan in 1979 it was decreed that Government workers should go coat-less and tie-less to the office in order to reduce the energy required for air conditioning. This, together with other measures, was expected to save around three million kilolitres of oil a year.

It is a sombre fact that the explosive power of nuclear weapons is so great that this has to be expressed in terms of the equivalent explosive power of thousands of tonnes of the high explosive TNT, ie kilotonnes of TNT.

Once Great Britain held the record for the longest ever sausage. This continuous pork sausage stretched for 3·21 km and weighed 1242 kg. The annual mean consumption of potatoes per head of population in Britain in 1984–85 (June to May) was 106·8 kg.

The Ordnance Survey maps of the United Kingdom have a grid consisting of squares representing length of side one kilometre.

A 2000 megawatt coal-fired power station on an average load of 60 per cent formerly emitted about 100 kilotonnes of sulphur dioxide per year, though improved practice has latterly, in the 1990s, reduced this.

mega (Greek, great) 10^6, symbol M

This prefix can be used to replace where appropriate the term 'million', thus: a million volts can be termed 1 MV (megavolt). In the case of electrical resistance where the name of the unit (ohm) begins with a vowel, the quantity one million ohms is specified as one megohm. A common use of the mega- prefix occurs in the electricity supply industry. The power output of electric generators is usually expressed in megawatts (millions of watts). The Sizewell B nuclear generator that came on power on 31 January 1995 reached an output of 1188 MW when fully commissioned.

Geologists and other scientists dealing with events over a long period of time make use of the Megayear (Myr). Typical values for the age of certain rocks might be 180 Myr (Jurassic period), or 350 Myr (Carboniferous period).

In 1981 the Argentine Central Bank issued a new one million peso banknote; this would be one megapeso. With modern large computers one may talk in terms of 'megaflops'. One megaflop is one million arithmetic operations per second.

Electronic storage and laser disc storage of the contents of documents has now reached a stage of development that the information on over a million A4 typed pages can be stored. One manufacturer has called his electronic archive a 'Megadoc'. A sinister use of the prefix mega arises from the development of nuclear weapons in the megatonne range. The aggressive use of such weapons would result in many megadeaths.

In all the above cases 'mega' means precisely one million. There has recently come into use the prefix 'mega' to denote anything very big: that is, it is used in a qualitative and not quantitative sense. The following are some examples of this practice: the amalgamation of large stockbrokers in the City of London has resulted in the description of such organisations as 'megabrokers'. A newspaper headline concerning a pop star read 'Soon to be a Megastar'. Another contribution read, 'The grand-daddy of the UN megaconferences was the United Nations Conference in Stockholm'.

giga (Greek, gigantic) 10^9, symbol G

A quantity with this prefix means a thousand million, that is 1 000 000 000. In the USA this number would be called one billion. It is a regrettable fact that many people in the United Kingdom are now using the word billion in the American sense in connection with money, mainly due to the predominance of the American dollar in world finance. This gradual replacement of the UK billion (10^{12}) by the American billion (10^9) is very unfortunate; there was no definite transitional date. The result is that readers of recent times and in the future will find it difficult to know which number was meant when they come across the word 'billion' in newspapers, periodicals, and even professional journals. The complete abolition of the word 'billion' should be quite easy, by introducing the prefix giga for the USA billion and tera (10^{12}) for the original UK billion.

In France the USA billion (10^9) is called the 'milliard'. This term has actually been used in Britain since 1823. The term milliard has been used in recent times in connection with the imports of natural gas by members of the European Community; examples of contracts for imports from the former Soviet Union have been quoted as follows: the former Federal Republic of Germany, in milliards of cubic metres, 10·7; Italy 7; and France 4.

The following are some examples of the use of the prefix giga. An idea of the order of magnitude of the number of locusts in a large swarm is about $60 \times 10^9 = 60$ gigalocusts. The largest swarm recorded was 400 gigalocusts with an estimated weight of 800 000 tonnes.

The plant capacity for the generation of electricity in the UK is over 50 GW (gigawatts). Particle accelerators have now been built to produce energies of more than 400 GeV (gigaelectron volts). The population of China was estimated to be 1·25 gigapersons (1996). In the UK the annual consumption of sausages in 1984 was 6000 million, which is six gigasausages.

Toshiba, a Japanese electronics company, has developed a digital video disc (DVD) with a storage capacity of 18 gigabytes. In July 1995 the video games company Sega declared its intention to adopt the Toshiba DVD format.

As in the case of mega, the word giga has been used in a qualitative sense. The absurdity of using the term billion is illustrated very well by a letter in *The Guardian* in December 1982. The author corrected a previous printing of a 'million' by 'billion'. He did not state whether this was a UK billion or a USA billion.

It was in the 1970s that most controversy arose concerning the use in the UK of the USA billion instead of the UK billion. This would seem to indicate that the billion in the above letter was the USA billion. But the fact that this letter of correction was necessary points to another disadvantage of using the word billion – which differs from the word million by but a single letter. Confusion can arise not only in telephone conversations but in announcements on the radio and television. [It seems now (1996) that the battle is decided, and that billion as in present use indicates 10^9. However, the word 'billion', whenever it is used must be examined and considered critically whenever past publications are consulted – Ed].

tera (from the Greek root meaning monstrous, marvel, prodigy) 10^{12}, symbol T

This prefix converts a unit into a million million (1 000 000 000 000). This corresponds to the true UK billion. [but see note above – Ed]

The distance denoted in astronomy by the term 'light year' is equal to 9460·5 Tm (terametres). In the United Kingdom the electrical energy generated by all the power stations controlled by the Central Electricity Generating Board amounted to 216·503 TWh (terawatt hours) in the year 1984–85. One of the proposed schemes for generating electricity by building a barrage across the River Severn would produce about 20 TWh per annum.

The *Aurora Borealis*, or Northern Lights, creates about 27 000 million kW hours of loose electricity across the sky every year. This means 27×10^{12} watt hours, ie 27 TWh.

The American usage of billion and trillion has led to the introduction of the American quadrillion. An example of the difficulty arising from the use of non-SI units was a report in 1981 in *The Times* stating that 'American energy production totalled 64·8 quadrillion (10^{15}) British thermal units'. Comparison with figures for energy in other contexts would have been easier had the figures been given in SI units with SI prefixes.

It was in 1948 that the International Weights and Measures Conference confirmed the traditional use of 'billion' and 10^{12} for all European languages; as had traditionally been the case. No such repudiation of the meaning has been agreed on an international basis. The use of the prefix tera would be a convenient method of superseding the term billion with its traditional meaning of 10^{12}.

peta, 10^{15}, symbol P

One prediction of the world consumption of energy in the 21st century is 28×10^{13} kWh per annum. This is equal to $280 \times 10^{15} = 280$ petawatt hours, which in symbols is 280 PWh.

exa, 10^{18}, symbol E

The volume of water in the oceans of the world is estimated to be about 1 370 000 000 cubic kilometres which equals $1·37 \times 10^{18}$ m^3 = 1370×10^{18} cubic decimetres or 1370×10^{18} litres = 1370 exalitres (designated as 1370 EL).

zetta, 10^{21}, symbol Z

The figure given above for the volume of water in the oceans of the world may be written as $1·37 \times 10^{21}$ litres which in symbols is 1·37 ZL.

yotta, 10^{24}, symbol Y

One estimate of the total energy radiated annually by the Sun is 4×10^{26} W. This is 400×10^{24} W = 400 yottawatts, which in symbols is 400 YW.

SI prefixes for sub-multiples of a base unit

There are two sub-multiple prefixes for numbers less than one thousandth. After the prefix milli signifying a thousandth, the subsequent prefixes indicate a geometric series 10^{-6}, 10^{-9}, 10^{-12}.

deci (Latin, tenth) 10^{-1}, symbol d

This is a prefix which has found relatively little application in the past. Its most important application in the future is likely to be for the cubic decimetre since this is the same as the litre.

Specialists in electroplating express current density in amperes per square decimetre. For nickel-plating the current density ranges from about 4 A dm^{-2} up to about 6·5 A dm^{-2}.

centi, (Latin, hundredth), 10^{-2}, symbol c

This is the non-preferred prefix which is likely to continue to be used extensively. The centimetre, for example, is not only a very convenient unit of length but is a base unit in all the c.g.s. systems of units in which there is a large volume of published scientific material.

The centilitre is used in commerce in some countries on the Continent of Europe.

The cost of advertisements in newspapers and periodicals is often quoted in terms of the price per centimetre of single column.

milli (Latin, thousandth), 10^{-3}, symbol m

The millilitre (ml or mL) is another name for the widely used cubic centimetre. The millimetre (mm) is the recommended unit of length for the use on engineering drawings, and for very many practical technological applications. The milligram (mg) is a widely used and convenient unit of mass in laboratory work and pharmacy. The millisecond (ms) is a convenient unit for timing many processes and events.

In the UK milk is, if sold in returnable glass bottles, supplied by the pint. Such milk bottles are marked thus: 1 pint, 568 ml: or 568 ml (in 1996).

After much confusion in the matter of the amount of wine that should constitute one glass of wine sold in a public house, the Government decided that there should be two standard sizes, one of 75 millilitres and the other of 125 millilitres. A measure of spirits is now usually 25 millilitres.

Some interesting experiments in the matter of touch by the human finger showed that the human sense of touch is sensitive enough to reveal a discontinuity only 0·001 mm high in an otherwise smooth surface, but when the change in height of the surface is a gentle hummock rather than a sharp edge, this ability is lost even for rather larger variations. With an undulation 3 mm wide and 0·0127 mm high, only 59·8 per cent of rubbing trials produced an accurate identification of the ridge and its orientation.

One cup of tea contains about 75 milligrams of caffeine; the corresponding figure for coffee is about 50 mg/cup for the 'instant' varieties but about double this value for ground coffee. These figures are intended to specify only the order of magnitude; cup sizes vary and hence an exact statement of the amount is not possible.

The legal minimum dimensions of sea fishing net meshes are specified in millimetres. It should be noted that a figure of, say 70 mm, denotes the dimension of the diagonal from one corner to another of the mesh.

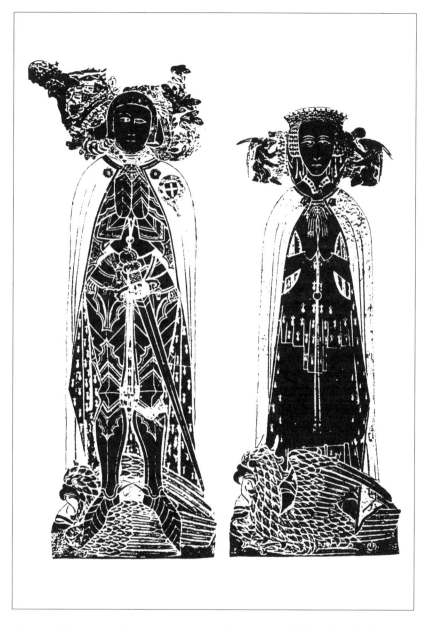

Figure 26 – A medieval monumental brass of 1483. The Earl of Essex and his wife, Little Easton, Essex.

micro (Greek, small) 10⁻⁶, symbol μ (mu)

This prefix attached to a unit denotes one millionth part of that unit: it has been found most useful in various branches of electronics. Thus the most widely used unit of electrical capacitance is the microfarad (μF).

The microgram (μg) is used to specify very small quantities of powerful drugs. The microsecond (μs) is extensively employed as a unit of time in electronics and other branches of physics. In electroplating, the thickness of the deposit is expressed in micrometres (μm), though the synonymous term microns is still often heard.

An American company has devised a miniature cell utilising the principle of the generation of electricity caused by difference in temperature. This thermo-electric generator is able to harness the temperature of the body to provide between 8 and 12 microwatts, which is at least a factor of five times the power necessary to drive a watch.

In connection with trace-elements in the human body, it was reported in 1983 that, on average, iodine contributions from milk intake had increased from 14 micrograms to more than 90 micrograms per person a day. One of the components of human blood are platelets, which are tiny disc-shaped cells 2 to 3 micrometres across and less than one micrometre thick.

In electronics there is a distinction made between thick films and thin films. The former range from about 12 micrometres up to about 25 micrometres, the latter are from about 0·25 to 1 micrometre.

An interesting hobby is the making of brass rubbings from medieval tombs. To determine losses and thus help safeguard the actual brass, measurements have been made to find out how much brass is lost in the process. This is about 0·12 μg cm⁻²; in terms of depth this means that the depth of brass removed per rubbing is about $1·8 \times 10^{-8}$ centimetres of brass or $1·8 \times 10^{-10}$ metre. See Figure 26 which illustrates such medieval brasses.

In February 1986 a leakage of radioactive plutonium nitrate occurred at Sellafield, Cumbria, when a reported 50 microcuries were released into the atmosphere.

nano (Greek, very small, Latin, dwarf) 10^{-9}, symbol n

This prefix attached to a unit means a quantity equal to that unit divided by a thousand million.

Visible light is of wavelength 400–700 nanometres (nm) [but see p272]. Green light as selected for photoelastic measurements of stress and strain has a wavelength of 488 nm. Ultra-violet radiation around wavelength 280 nm (UV-B) is about 5000 times more damaging to the human skin than uv light around 320 nm (UV-A). In free space light travels approximately 300 mm in one nanosecond.

Transient currents in electrical circuits of very short duration are conveniently measured for duration in ns (nanoseconds).

In *The Times* of 1 May 1995 there was a report of the advent of a blood test devised by a Dr William Catalona for prostate-specific antigen (PSA). Values of 0·5–4 ng/mL are normal, but readings over 10 ng/mL in a man's blood may suggest a 50% chance of malignancy of the prostate gland.

The values 0·1 nm and 100 nm are measures of the diameter of a hydrogen atom and the thickness of a sheet of fine gold leaf respectively. An electrical impulse in an insulated wire travels about 150 mm in one nanosecond. Nanotechnology is a branch of applied science which covers the manufacture, measurement and use of minute devices such as those that may eventually be introduced into, say, blood vessels.

pico (Spanish, a small quantity) 10^{-12}, symbol p

This prefix designates a unit divided by a million million, ie $1 \div 1\,000\,000\,000\,000$. At one time the smallest values of electrical capacitance were specified in micromicrofarads (symbol $\mu\mu$F). Since current practice avoids the use of double prefixes, this particular small value of capacitance is conveniently specified as the picofarad pF.

The most common application for this prefix is in connection with time; the following are some examples. A microchip has been produced that makes calculations in 80 picoseconds (1993). In 1981 American scientists produced a burst of light with a duration of less than 0·1 ps.

An example of the non-universal use of American terminology occurs in a report that American scientists have measured the short duration of one trillionth of a second which was explained as one thousand billionth, which is certainly not unambiguous. It might be taken to mean a duration of one thousand billionths of a second. It actually means 10^{-12} second or one picosecond.

femto, 10^{-15}, symbol f

The diameter of the proton (one of the two main sub-atomic particles in the nuclei of atoms) is approximately one femtometre, ie 1×10^{-15} metre.

atto, 10^{-18}, symbol a

The value of the charge on an electron is 0·16 attocoulomb (aC). Q, a unit used in measuring the total collision cross-section of electrons with atoms and molecules, has a value 0·88 attometre.

zepto, 10^{-21}, symbol z and yocto 10^{-24}, symbol y

These very small sub-multiples, particularly the last three mentioned, have very few applications, but they are included here for the sake of completeness.

Chapter V Part 3

The SI System of Units – Codes of Practice

Earlier and general recommendations

There are a number of recommendations that have been made by the various international bodies concerned with measurement and with standardisation, which aim at greater uniformity in practice amongst the various nations using SI units. Unfortunately some of these recommendations have been misconstrued as rules, and a certain amount of opposition to them has been engendered by those who have not noticed the difference between, for example, 'preferred' prefixes or symbols or derived units, and 'prohibited' practice. In particular is the mistaken impression that many people have had: that the centimetre is a prohibited unit. This has antagonised certain groups of people, particularly those who have tried to oppose the introduction of the whole process of metrication. The following points should therefore be considered in the light of the objective of the bodies making the recommendations, of which the ISO is the most important.

It was initially recommended by the ISO that certain prefixes would be 'preferred' ones. These were those the indices of which were integer multiples of 3 or −3. The inference was made by some people that the remaining prefixes were not to be used, though the idea behind the recommendation was merely to avoid excessive proliferation of multiples and submultiples in general practice, but not to prohibit the 'non-preferred' multiples and submultiples. These were the following: hecto, deca, deci and centi. Not all of these are likely to be used extensively. On the other hand some non-preferred sub-multiples are almost certain to find widespread use. The most important of these clearly is the centimetre (cm). There is no doubt about the validity of claims that this particular sub-multiple will survive. In physics, chemistry and the applied sciences it has very widespread application, and it is, of course, the base unit of length in the various c.g.s. systems, of which there is a vast literature. In education it seems certain that the first unit of length that a child will meet in the infant school will be the centimetre. The millimetre is too small to handle in terms of, for example, most models; the metre is too large: and the centimetre is an ideal premise of length for deriving area and volume. Many practical cases will arise where the centimetre will be the most convenient unit of length compared with the millimetre or the metre.

A non-preferred metric unit of length which is likely to persist in certain particular fields is the Ångstrom, equal to 10^{-10} metre. The nearest SI unit of length to the Ångstrom is the nanometre, equal to 10^{-9} metre, so that 1Å could be called 1/10 nm; alternatively to avoid decimal parts, the Å could be called 100 pm since 1 picometre $= 10^{-12}$ metre. A preferred sub-multiple which has been used extensively under another name is the micrometre (μm) which has been known for many years as a micron.

In the case of engineering drawings, there is wide acceptance of the millimetre as the unit in which all dimensions on drawings shall be expressed. In a very large number of practical cases, this means that no decimal points will be necessary.

The use of whole numbers for measurements in millimetres would not apply, of course, to those rarer cases where precision warrants values expressed in parts of a millimetre. This point applies in several other realms of measurement. Account should be taken in practical cases of what constitutes a 'significant difference' when a measurement is made. Take the so-called 'vital statistics' of a lady. If the preferred sub-multiple of the metre is used, the figures could be, for example 920 mm, 600 mm, 920 mm. No one supposes that such measurements would actually be made to the nearest millimetre; the centimetre would be a reasonable 'significant difference', particularly in view of the fact that the present significant difference is an inch. It would seem advisable, therefore, in these circumstances to use the centimetre and make the ladies happier with say, 92, 60, 92!

There are a number of recommendations for users of SI which relate to the writing, typing, or printing of symbols, abbreviations, etc.

As previously indicated, only a single prefix should be used in connection with any one quantity. For example, a thousandth of a millimetre is not called one millimillimetre but one micrometre (μm). In one case, of course, the base unit has a prefix; and even here 1000 of these units, ie 1000 kilograms, needs to be specified as one megagram (Mg) and not one kilokilogram. This particular quantity can alternatively be called one tonne – sometimes referred to as the metric ton.

It should be noted that whilst the full forms of units admit to plurals, the symbols do not take the plural form. Thus 18 hbar is correct, but when written in full as part of a sentence it is correct to write 18 hectobars. The absence of the letter s from the plural form of a symbol eliminates a possible source of doubt or confusion where the letter s might be taken to be the symbol for the unit of time – the second – for which the symbol is the letter s. For example, the plural of kg is also kg and not kgs; which might be mistaken for kg s, denoting flow rate.

A space is used between a number and its unit symbol thus: 250 A, not 250A. Strictly speaking this should be a half-space and printers can provide this, but many typewriters and typesetters cannot comply. [In the preparation of these two volumes it was decided to type-set with a full space -Ed.]

There are two exceptions to this 'space' rule; in respect of angles and temperatues. Thus when denoting an angle, thus: 45°, 1°27′ and 2°14′36″; and when temperatures are expressed, as in 100°C, for example. The general question of writing symbols and abbreviations correctly assumes great importance when looked at from the point of view of the maintenance of international agreement and full understanding. It might be difficult for the newspaper journalists and for members of the general public to adhere rigidly to the various conventions agreed upon by international bodies; but schools, colleges, and every kind of educational body should co-operate with the scientific and technological bodies in fostering uniform practice in this direction. It might appear pedantic to some people that the use of a capital letter instead of a small letter should introduce error; but this can be very important. The following are simple matters which ought to be noticed and adhered to.

The agreed abbreviations for the various units in SI are not written with capital letters, except where they commemorate a person, the so-called memorial names. Thus we have kg, m and s; but N for newton, W for watt, J for joule, etc. Notice that the full memorial name is not written with a capital; only its symbol. Other agreed conventions are as follows.

There are no full stops ('points') between letters in such abbreviations as SI, CGPM, NPL, etc. There should be no hyphenating of multiples of units, as for example milligram (and not milli-gram). Not more than one solidus should be used, thus:

cm/s^2 and not cm/s/s $g/s\ cm^{-1}$ and not g/s/cm

In fact modern practise deprecates the use of the solidus so $cm\ s^{-2}$ is preferred to cm/s^2; and $g\ s^{-1}\ cm^{-1}$ to $g/s\ cm^{-1}$.

Quite a number of former styles of symbolism and abbreviation which have been used in the past are now deemed incorrect, and their persistence should be discouraged. Thus kilo was at one time a common designation for kilogramme but the current approved abbreviation is kg and the spelling of the full name of the unit is kilogram.

When in a practical case a choice is possible between two adjacent multiples or submultiples in which to express the information concerned, it is recommended that the choice should be such that the numerical values concerned should lie between 0·1 and 1000. Suppose, for example, that the production of a given commodity in unit time increased in a decade from 700 kg to 75 000 kg. This statement could be made to conform to the above recommendation by being given as 'from 0·7 Mg to 75 Mg'. A less satisfactory way of expressing this statement would be to say 'from 700 kg to 75 Mg' since this conveys a less distinct impression of the growth than the other statements. There would be some cases where the recommended practice would not be appropriate. This could arise in the case of long tables of statistics which might need to be fitted into another pattern of data: it will often be found that the range of numerical values exceeds 1 to 10 000, and the recommendation being discussed is then not applicable.

The 1967 Recommendations of the CIPM

Since multiples and submultiples of SI units are in such widespread use, it is just as well to observe the following recommendations on nomenclature adopted by the CIPM in 1967:

1. The appellation 'International System of Units' and its abbreviation SI designate the whole ensemble of units, including the decimal multiples and submultiples.

2. In this appellation the word 'system' consequently has the meaning 'systematically organised' and is not limited to use in referring to the coherent part of the system.

3. The base, supplementary and derived units, which form a coherent ensemble, are to be designated as 'Units of the International System' with the abbreviation 'SI Units'.

4. The decimal multiples and submultiples of the SI Units are to be designated as 'multiples and submultiples of SI units'.

The supplementary dimensionless units of SI are as follows:

quantity	SI unit	unit symbol
angle	radian	rad
solid angle	steradian	sr

Some people have taken this matter to mean that plane angles must always be specified in radians. There are many physical formulae where this is necessarily the case, but there will continue to be extensive use of degrees, minutes and seconds of angle in other cases. This style of unit was classified by the CIPM in 1969 as one of a group under the heading of non-SI units which can continue to be used indefinitely. This situation is unaltered in the 1986 rules.[178]

The 'grade' system of measurements for angles is used in some continental countries; it is sometimes called the 'centesimal' system to distinguish it from the 'sexagesimal' system based on 60. The basic relationship is:

100 grade (100^g) = 1 right angle
400^g = 1 revolution or complete circle.

Submultiples are:

$100^{cc} = 1^c$ $100^c = 1^g$.

Alternative ways of expressing an angular measurement would then be for example, 274^g, 63^c, 85^{cc} or 274·6385 grades. The submultiple $1 \div 100$ grade, the centigrade, has been confused with the centigrade unit of temperature. The name grade has therefore been changed to gon. The term centigrade for temperature is, of course, supplanted by Celsius in modern nomenclature.

It is most important not to confuse the International System with the Metric Technical System. The latter is a gravitational system and has been used extensively on the Continent of Europe. By international agreement users of the Metric Technical System will phase out the use of these units, so that eventually there will be in general use only one metric system throughout the world, (excluding during the next few years USA and a few small countries which at the present time are of relatively small commercial importance). In the Metric Technical System there are recognised units being both kilogram mass and kilogram force, with all the consequent disadvantages of similar gravitational systems. Thus one must write kg for the mass unit abbreviation and kgf for the force unit; some use has been made of the name 'kilopond' for the latter, since 'kgf' has not always been used when it should have been. All this can be very confusing, and the need to keep introducing g = 9·806 65 where gravity does not enter into consideration is hardly reassuring to those who are not clear about the reason for doing this. As with the imperial systems using the same name for force and mass, the Metric Technical System is non-coherent. It is most important that intending users of SI should be aware of the existence of this other metric system which uses the kilogram as the unit of mass.

At an international conference on the subject of MKS units held in Brussels in 1968 a delegate from the Republic of Ireland introduced a little humour into the conference proceedings. He proposed the introduction of a new base unit, namely one for the measurement of feminine beauty! This he proposed to call the Helen, presumably after Helen of Troy. It would seem that an average girl or lady would be rated at somewhere between 1 helen and 1 hectohelen. A beautiful woman could find herself in the kilohelen class, whilst a world figure like Greta Garbo would be rated in the megahelen range. [It has also been suggested that the millihelen is the measure of a face that can launch one ship! – Ed].

The CIPM deprecates the use, in conjunction with SI units, of those c.g.s. units which have special names. It recognises that in certain specialised branches of science there may be good reasons for using some of these, but puts great emphasis on uniformity regarding symbols whatever system of units is being employed. Table XIII shows the c.g.s. units referred to above.

Table XIII

c.g.s. units with special names

name of unit	symbol	value in SI units
erg	erg	10^{-7} joule
dyne	dyn	10^{-5} newton
poise	P	$0·1$ pascal second
stokes	St	10^{-4} metre^2 second^{-1}
gauss	G or Gs	10^{-4} tesla
oersted	Oe	$1000/4\,\pi$ ampere metre^{-1}
maxwell	Mx	10^{-8} weber
stilb	sb	10^4 candela metre^{-2}
phot	ph	10^4 lux

It is necessary to recognise, outside the International System, some other units that are useful in specialised fields. Although their values may be expressed in SI units, they must be obtained by experiment and such values are therefore not known exactly. See Table XVI

The electron volt is the kinetic energy acquired by an electron in passing through a potential difference of 1 volt *in vacuo*:

$$1 \text{ eV} = 1·602\ 19 \times 10^{-19} \text{ J approximately.}$$

The unified atomic mass unit is equal to 1/12 of the mass of an atom of the nuclide carbon–12. 1 u = $1\cdot660\,57 \times 10^{-27}$ kg approximately.

Table XIV
Other units generally deprecated

name of unit	value in SI units
metric carat	1 metric carat = 200 mg = 2×10^{-4} kg
fermi	1 fermi = 1 fm = 10^{-15} m
torr	1 torr = (101 325/760) Pa
standard atmosphere (atm)	1 atm = 101 325 Pa
kilogram-force (kgf)	1 kgf = $9\cdot806\,65$ N
calorie (cal)	1 calorie = $4\cdot186\,8$ joules
micron (μ)	1 μ = 1 μm = 10^{-6} m
X unit (Siegbahn unit)	1 X unit = $1\cdot00202 \times 10^{-9}$ m
stere (st)	1 st = 1 m^3
gamma (γ)	1 γ = 1 pT = 10^{-12} T
gamma (γ)	1 γ = 1 μg = 10^{-9} kg
lambda (λ)	1 λ = 1 μL = 10^{-6} L = 1^{-9} m^3

Table XV
Units in use temporarily with the International System

name	symbol	value in SI units
nautical mile		1 nautical mile = 1852 m
knot		1 nautical mile per hour = (1852/3600) m s^{-1}
angström	Å	1 Å = $0\cdot1$ nm = 10^{-10} m
are	a	1 a = 1 dam^2 = 10^2 m^2
hectare	ha	1 ha = 1 hm^2 = 10^4 m^2
barn	b	1 b = 100 fm^2 = 10^{-28} m^2
bar	bar	1 bar = $0\cdot1$ MPa = 100 kPa = 1000 hPa = 10^5 Pa
gal	Gal	1 Gal = 1 cm/s^2 = 10^{-2} m s^{-2}
curie	Ci	1 Ci = $3\cdot7 \times 10^{10}$ Bq
röntgen	R	1 R = $2\cdot58 \times 10^{-4}$ C kg^{-1}
rad	rad	1 rad = 1 cGy = 10^{-2} Gy
rem	rem	1 rem = 1 cSv = 10^{-2} Sv

Table XVI

Units used with the International System, equivalent values in SI units, obtained experimentally

name	symbol
electron volt	eV
unified atomic mass unit	u

Chapter VI

Some useful derived units in SI

Introduction

This chapter is a short review of the more common derived units and some of the applications related to topical areas of human concern; more particularly thermal energy, ionizing radiation, measures of concentration of substances, pressure and illumination. Measurements of these, and related phenomena may be quantified in terms of SI units. Moreover, rigorous comparisons become easier when such quoted units that have world-wide recognition are adopted for such measurements.

Thermal energy

It is important to realise that the joule in SI is the universal unit of energy (kinetic or potential, bond energy, electrical energy and whatever) in any or all of its forms. The following are some items employing the joule as a unit of potential or kinetic or heat energy.

Food

For many years there has been a recurring mistake in the specification of the energy content of food by using the word 'Calorie'. 1 Calorie (capital C) = 1000 × calorie (small c). The quantity Calorie (sometimes called the great calorie) should be the kilocalorie. The mistake will gradually be eliminated as the kilocalorie or Calorie (now obsolescent in the UK) gives way to the kilojoule. One kilocalorie is equivalent to about 4·2 kilojoules [see Table XII, page 215]. Modern food manufacturers now specify the energy content of their products in kilojoules (kJ), though the use of Calories (implying kilocalories) is still common on food packaged in the USA (1996).

Thermal resistance

With heat energy expressed in joules, the flow of heat energy from one place to another is very conveniently expressed in joules per second, or watts. The clothes worn by human beings generally have as their main purpose that of keeping the body warm. We thus introduce the idea of thermal resistance, that is the resistance offered by the clothes to the flow of heat from the body to the outside.

It has been found convenient in the textile industry particularly, but also in other applications, to consider the thermal resistance offered by one square metre of fabric; or other materials such as those used in the building industry.

The root cause of the net heat flow is the temperature difference between two surfaces. The resistance to the heat flow is measured in terms of how few watts flow when unit temperature difference exists between the two faces. In SI this would be K (kelvin) divided by the resultant heat flow in watts.

For textiles it has been found convenient to introduce a practical unit for thermal resistance per unit area. This unit, called the tog, is defined as follows. One tog means that the flow of heat through one square metre of fabric under test is 10 joules per second or 10 watts when the temperature difference between opposite sides of the fabric is one degree on the Celsius scale, that is one kelvin (1K). Table XVII shows some typical examples of values of thermal resistance.

The most widespread application of the tog comes in the specifications of the values of thermal resistance of bed coverings. Table XVIII gives some examples of the thermal ratings of continental quilts or duvets.

Table XVII

Thermal resistance of certain materials

material	thickness (mm)	weight (g/m²)	togs
cotton poplin shirting	0·43	105	0·09
locknit wool vest	2·21	328	0·55
cellular cotton vest	4·45	180	0·89
melton overcoating	3·43	662	0·78
velour overcoating	6·10	645	1·53
raised wool blanket	8·03	617	2·18
leno cotton blanket	5·31	285	1·31
Axminster wool carpet	12·83	2240	2·52
tufted viscose carpet	9·40	2160	1·55

(Test pressure $6·9$ N/m² (pascals))

When the same net heat flow passes through two materials in succession, these two materials are said to be 'in series'. Since values of thermal resistance of articles in series can be summated, advantage was taken of this fact by some manufacturers to design a quilt in two parts. The 'summer' part has a rating of 4·5 togs, the 'autumn' (and 'spring') part has a rating of 7·0 togs. In winter the two are combined to give a rating of 11·5 togs.

Table XVIII

Tog rating of quilts

natural filling		synthetic filling	
new feather and down	10·5 togs	polyester	9·5 togs
new duck feather and soft duck down	10·0 togs	terylene	11·5 togs
new duck down	12·5 togs		
new white goose down	13·5 togs		

A very far cry from all this scientific precision demanded in relation to ambient temperatures is the unit of 'cold' said to persist amongst a tribe of aborigines in Australia. This unit is called the 'dog'. It appears that to keep warm during the night, members of this tribe use live dogs in place of blankets. A moderately chilly night would be rated by them as a 'two-dog night', whilst a keen frosty night would be a 'six-dog night'!

Cost of energy

In the past it has been difficult for industrial, commercial and domestic consumers of energy to make a fair comparison between the unit prices of gas, electricity, oil and solid fuel. The electricity meter measures kilowatt-hours and the gas meter measures cubic feet of gas. Oil is sold by volume and solid fuel by weight. It ought to be possible to make comparison of unit costs by comparing the cost of energy, in each case specified by the same unit. For domestic consumers the megajoule (MJ) would suit this purpose. In all cases, present methods of selling the energy need not be changed; all that is required is a statement on the bill giving the cost in pence per megajoule. [Another alternative is for the cost per kilowatt hour to be specified, a practice that occurs increasingly: 1 kilowatt hour = 3·6 megajoules -- Ed.]

Ionizing radiation

When an atomic nucleus undergoes fission, sub-atomic particles and electromagnetic rays are emitted, the nature of which depends upon the type of atom. There are usually three types of such emissions; viz alpha particles (helium nucleii), beta particles (electrons or positrons) and gamma radiation (very short wavelength electromagnetic radiation). The degree of effect on the human body or other organisms of these different nuclear emissions differs radically because of their different associated energies. In all cases their effects are to disrupt DNA chains (or occasionally RNA chains), which constitute the genetic material. The damage may be slight and not significant, but may be profound or even irreparable. Alpha particles are relatively large – over 7000 times the mass of beta particles – and cannot travel far in the air, still less through human tissue. The greatest danger of alpha-emitters occurs if they are ingested.

Beta particles travel short distances in the air, and some little distance through human tissue. Gamma radiation is highly penetrative, being stopped only by thick shields, of concrete or lead for instance.

Units for the measurement of nuclear radiation

In view of the fact that obsolescent units of radiation have continued to be used long after the present units have been defined, it is necessary to outline their history.

The first unit of nuclear disintegration was rather large because early measurements of radiation were relatively crude. The curie was defined as 3.7×10^{10} disintegrations per second. The roentgen was the unit of radiation exposure. An exposure dose of 1 roentgen corresponds to about 9.4×10^{-3} J absorbed per kg of target living tissue. It was defined as the amount of radiation that produced one electrostatic unit of ions per cubic centimetre of volume (c 1960).

The effect of any type of ionizing radiation ray or particle depends on at least two factors: the target material and the energy of the increment of radiation. A new unit was coined called the rad. Its origin can be traced back to 1918, when Russ suggested that the unit of x-rays should be that dose required to kill a mouse, and that the unit should be called the rad. The rad was more precisely defined in 1953 (in c.g.s. units) and in 1970 (in SI units): viz the absorbed dose is 1 rad when 1 kilogram of exposed material absorbs 10^{-2} joules of energy. An exposure dose of 1 roentgen in human soft body tissue is about 0.0096 mJ/g, equal to very nearly 1 rad. Thus for radiological protection purposes, the units may be regarded as equivalent, or nearly so.

A unit proposed by H M Parker about 1950 was the rem (from roentgen equivalent man). It took some account of the differing types and energies of the radiation in question. The unit is obsolete.

The modern units in the field of ionizing radiation are those defined by the CGPM and are all SI units. In 1974 the CGPM defined the unit of nuclear disintegration as one disintegration per second and called this unit the becquerel, symbol Bq. For the unit of absorbed dose, the CIPM proposed in 1974 the gray. The gray replaced the rad: 1 gray equals 100 rad.

In 1980 the sievert, symbol Sv, was adopted to avoid the confusion between absorbed dose and dose equivalent. It was defined as follows: the sievert is the SI unit of dose equivalent in the field of radio-protection and is equal to one joule per kilogram. The sievert is derived from the gray by multiplying the value in grays by a factor appropriate to the type of radio-source. The factor is 20 for alpha radiation, and unity for beta and gamma radiation. This former factor of 20 acknowledges the fact that alpha-emitters are particularly dangerous, since the mass and dimensions of the alpha particle are high. The sievert replaces the obsolete rem; 1 Sv = 100 rem. It may be noted that a typical natural background radiation exposure for a UK inhabitant is about 2 millisieverts per annum. A worker at a nuclear power plant may receive up to 50 millisieverts per annum. A radiograph of the chest may deliver about 0·1 millisievert.

The National Radiological Protection Board was set under *The Radiological Protection Act 1970*. See its title page – Figure 28, p257.

The Chernobyl disaster: reports in 1986, 1988 and 1992

Initial reports on the infamous catastrophe at the nuclear power station at Chernobyl in the former USSR (now in Belorussia) on 26 April 1986 created widespread confusion in the media, caused largely by lack of knowledge of what radiation is and the units used to measure it. Two of the units used by the Russians in the early report of the event were even then obsolete, viz the curie and the roentgen. Leonid Ilyn, Director of the Institute of Biophysics in Moscow, reported on some human victims' exposure in the following terms (now known to be inaccurate): the most serious cases were those who had been exposed to 2000 roentgens of radioactivity or more, which led to a breakdown of the central nervous system; those exposed to 200 to 1500 roentgens exhibited severe vomiting, and after apparent recovery became ill again.

Figure 27 – Report from The Times *(29 April 1986) of the Chernobyl incident.* © *Times Newspapers Limited, 1986.*

Huge nuclear leak at Soviet plant

By Thomson Prentice, Science Correspondent, and Christopher Mosey, Stockholm

A massive radioactive leak at a Soviet nuclear power station has caused casualties in what may be the world's worst nuclear accident. The leak was so large that it prompted a full-scale alert nearly 1,000 miles away in Sweden, including the evacuation of 600 workers from a Swedish power station on the Baltic coast.

Finland reported radiation levels six times higher than normal, Denmark five times higher than normal, and Norway 50% up as a result of the accident. "We have registered radiation just about everywhere we have looked," said Mr Ragnar Boge, of the Swedish Radiation Institute.

Soviet atomic energy authorities at first told the Swedish Embassy in Moscow they were unaware of any nuclear accident on Soviet territory that could cause a leak to reach Sweden.

But later Tass reported that an accident had taken place at a nuclear power station at Chernobyl, north of Kiev, and there were some casualties.

It said measures were being undertaken "to eliminate the consequences of the accident" at the plant, where a reactor had been damaged. Aid was being given to those affected by the leak and a government committee of inquiry had been set up.

Swedish scientists at first believed a leak had occurred at their own nuclear plant at Forsmark, on the Baltic coast

about 60 miles north of Stockholm, and evacuated the 600 workers there. After the evacuation radiation levels were checked at other areas of the country, including the capital.

These all confirmed a higher degree of radioactivity than normal, and further tests at Forsmark led the Swedish authorities to conclude that the discharge had come from the Soviet Union.

Some Swedish nuclear experts said they believed the Soviet accident was caused by the overheating of nuclear fuel. A "considerable explosion" would be the result of such overheating and could have led to a "meltdown" of the nuclear core of the reactor.

The Swedish Energy Minister, Mrs Birgitta Dahl, said all Russian nuclear reactors should be placed under inter-

national control."We must demand that the Soviet Union improve their security and inform the rest of the world in good time."

The first stage of the Chernobyl nuclear plant was put into service in September 1977, followed by two more stages in 1980.

The Swedish Defence Ministry said an abnormally high level of radioactivity had been recorded yesterday afternoon by several monitoring stations in Finland, Sweden, Denmark and Norway.

The ministry said that at a rate of "a few millirems an hour" the level was not thought high enough to warrant the evacuation of the local population at Forsmark. It would not be a danger to human beings, although regional specialists said the level

was twice as high in Finland as in Sweden and Norway.

A millirem is a unit of ionizing radiation that gives the same biological effect as one thousandth of a standard unit of X-rays.

● **MOSCOW:** Tass said the accident was the first of its kind in the Soviet Union (Christopher Walker writes).

Since Mr Mikhail Gorbachov came to power in March 1985 there have been repeated calls in the Soviet press for more open reporting of disasters inside the country.

The Tass statement was seen as a quick propaganda move ordered by the Kremlin to counter any international criticism of safety measures taken inside the Soviet Union, which has always been secretive about its nuclear programme.

Although there was no official indication here of the seriousness of the incident, Westerners in telephone contact with Kiev said early today morning that civilian buses had been commandeered from the city to evacuate citizens from the immediate area. The plant, with at least four 1,000 megawatt reactors, is situated on a reservoir some 30 miles north of the city.

Western diplomats speculated that the sharp jumps in radiation levels in Scandinavia pointed to the possibility of great dangers to those living closer to the accident area.

Background reports, page 9

Figure 27a – Detail.

The Watt Committee Report and subsequent revelations

The Report of the Watt Committee published in 1988 gave an account of the Chernobyl accident in terms of modern units (though the 1992 account in *Izvestia*, see *post*, shows that the Watt Committee account is suspect due to the disinformation that came into its hands).[169, 170B] A summary of the main points is as follows. In this disaster there was a massive release of radioactive nuclides, due to a succession of errors. Power intended at the 700 to 1000 MW (thermal) level fell to 30 MW (thermal) during an ill-considered test. In regaining power, to 2000 MW (thermal), the operator was forced to run the boron carbide control rods (which limits the nuclear chain reaction) further out than was safe or permitted. Alternate excesses and deficits of water and steam in the reactor, and also protection devices that had been deliberately disabled, led the inherently unstable reactor conditions to rise in power: soon the nuclear reactor reached a calculated 100 times nominal full power.

An explosive release of steam lifted the reactor top shield and released the core debris into the environment. Atmospheric air entered, following which there was an explosion, possibly part-chemical, that destroyed the containment building. A graphite fire followed which further vaporized the radioactive fission products. The atomic power pulse was low: it was fortunately terminated, ie to become sub-critical, early in the sequence of events because the fission material came to be so rapidly dispersed. However the combination of explosive steam, the explosion and the graphite fire all assured a horrendously large release of nuclear fission products. In the vicinity of Chernobyl two persons died in the accident, whilst 29 died of beta exposure-related maladies. 271 other people were hospitalized due to the accident, 174 of them with radiation-related symptons.

In some cases a bone-marrow transplant improves the chance of survival because it restores the body's capability to make blood cells after the marrow has been damaged by high doses of radiation. 13 people who had suffered very high radiation doses of between 5·6 and 13·4 grays (Gy) were given bone-marrow transplants. 11 of these patients did not survive. This is not surprising since a radiation dose of only 3 to 4 Gy will kill 50% of those people affected. Of 135 000 persons evacuated from a 30 km zone around Chernobyl, an estimated 1000 could develop fatal cancers in the decades following. In 1989 it was announced from Moscow that 250 of these people had already died.

According to the (highly suspect) Soviet reports to the International Atomic Energy Commission the release of radioactive material on the first day of the accident was (with an uncertainty factor of about 2) as follows:

iodine–131	0·7 EBq	($0·7 \times 10^{18}$ becquerel)
tellurium–132	0·15 EBq	($0·15 \times 10^{18}$ becquerel)
caesium–134	0·0055 EBq	($0·0055 \times 10^{18}$ becquerel)
caesium–137	0·011 EBq	($0·011 \times 10^{18}$ becquerel)

(total of all radioactive material 0·83 EBq.)

Radioactive releases fell to about one-third of these levels during the six days following, though day 8 and day 10 again saw levels rise to some $0·7 \times 10^{18}$ becquerels (0·7 EBq or 700 PBq).

However, in 1992 it was revealed that there had been a cover-up in the matter of the magnitude of the disaster at Chernobyl. Much of the detail of the true, or truer, position appeared in the pages of the Russian paper *Izvestia*. The number of persons affected by dangerous radiation was very much higher than the number stated in the official reports just after the disaster. Instead of the 1882 persons taken to hospital as officially reported, the true number was 10 198. The number suffering from acute radiation sickness had been given as 197 but the actual number was 345. Even this was not a true picture because the original defined radiation dose indicating radiation sickness was raised to ten times that value. At its ninth anniversary on 26 April 1995 the Ukraine Health Minister Andrei Serdyuk asserted that 125 000 people in the Ukraine had died as a result of the Chernobyl incident.

The Times on 26 September 1995 carried a report of remarks to the United Nations by Uladzimir Syanko, Belorussia's Foreign Minister. He reported that over 20% of his country's national budget was used in coping with the after-effects of the Chernobyl catastrophe, that genetic diseases were conspicuously on the rise, and that the birthrate in Belorussia had fallen by 50 percent.

The extent to which food had been contaminated was also much greater than had been reported originally. Special steps were taken to distribute this food over as wide an area as possible in order to prevent a large accumulation of radiation in the bodies of local people from the consumption of contaminated food.

As clouds from the Chernobyl area drifted across Britain in the few days after 26 April 1986, precipitation caused 'hot-spots' of radiation in certain area, most particularly in North Wales and Cumbria. The resulting contamination of sheep necessitated monitoring and restrictions on their sale for some eight years, until 1994.

Reports ten years after the Chernobyl incident suggest that the wrecked reactor building constitutes a hazard that will demand continuous monitoring for up to one hundred thousand years. (BBC, *Horizon*, April 1996).

Irradiation of food

There is a useful application of ionizing radiation given in doses which are carefully monitored. Radiation (usually gamma radiation) applied to the selected food can kill bacteria and other microorganisms and so make the food safer by preventing spoilage. There has been in the United Kingdom strong opposition to the irradiation of food, but this practice has been permissible in many other countries.

In 1989 a draft directive from the EEC on food irradiation was under consideration by the Westminster Parliament. Mr J MacGregor, the then Minister of Agriculture, Fisheries and Food, stated that the draft directive was fundamentally correct; it would be a useful extra weapon for ensuring food safety. The EEC Committee for Food had evaluated the safety of the process. It set an upper limit of 10 000 grays (10 kGy) which is deemed to be sufficient to kill all known bacteria: but see below. Actual values necessary to kill 90% of the various types of microbes in food range from 130 grays to 5000 grays.

In an undated (c 1994) leaflet *Food Irradiation* published by The Food Safety Advisory Service, Professor Campbell-Platt of the University of Reading states that 50 kGy would be required to kill the spores of *Clostridium botulinum*, an organism that produces an

1454   c. 46

Radiological Protection Act 1970

1970 CHAPTER 46

An Act to provide for the establishment of a National Radiological Protection Board and an Advisory Committee, with functions concerning the protection of people from radiation hazards; and for connected purposes.   [29th May 1970]

BE IT ENACTED by the Queen's most Excellent Majesty, by and with the advice and consent of the Lords Spiritual and Temporal, and Commons, in this present Parliament assembled, and by the authority of the same, as follows:—

The National Radiological Protection Board and its functions.

1.—(1) There shall be a public authority, to be called the National Radiological Protection Board (in this Act referred to as " the Board "), whose function it shall be—

(*a*) by means of research and otherwise, to advance the acquisition of knowledge about the protection of mankind from radiation hazards ; and

(*b*) to provide information and advice to persons (including government departments) with responsibilities in the United Kingdom in relation to the protection from radiation hazards either of the community as a whole or of particular sections of the community.

(2) The Board shall have power—

(*a*) to provide technical services to persons concerned with radiation hazards ; and

(*b*) to make charges for such services, and for providing information and advice.

(3) The foregoing subsections shall not be treated as transferring to the Board any functions exercisable by a government department under any enactment ; but the Board shall, in

Figure 28 – Title page of Radiological Protection Act 1970.

extremely poisonous toxin. Campbell-Platt continues, 'This level of dose produces quite unacceptable changes in the colour and flavour of treated food. Hence at a level of irradiation of 10 kGy *Clostridium botulinum* will not be completely eliminated . . . we therefore must prevent germination and growth. To do this food must be kept chilled or we must increase the acidity level of the food.'

Opposition to the use of radiation in food is understandable, not least because human beings cannot withstand anything like the high values necessary to kill microorganisms. Values of absorbed dose of radiation as low as 4 grays can be fatal to most people. Irradiation of some foods alters them chemically, so that they taste and look different. Some vitamins, particularly A, C, E, thiamin and pyridoxine are progressively destroyed by irradiation. In accordance with the EEC directive, irradiation of food in the United Kingdom became legal on 1 January 1991. Good practice dictates that no food is irradiated more than once.

Radiation in relation to mass

Questions were raised in 1977 concerning any danger of silt in the estuary near Ravenglass, close to the nuclear reprocessing plant at Sellafield, in Cumbria. It was stated that the concentration of plutonium rose steadily from 1966 to 1970, but remained steady thereafter at about 0·12 microcurie per kilogram. Plutonium is a particularly dangerous material: 100 micrograms is a potentially lethal dose.

After the Chernobyl accident, some meat contaminated with caesium–137 to a level of 6000 becquerels per kilogram was sold in Moscow. Some eight years after the disaster and at a distance of over 2200 km, lambs in England, Wales and Scotland were found to be over the internationally agreed 'safe' limit of 1000 becquerels per kilogram. Tests on grouse in August 1986 revealed levels of 75 to 328 becquerels per kilogram. The 'safe' level of radioactivity in milk in the UK, as set by the Government, is 2000 Bq/L.

Radiation in unit time

A factor that sets contaminations by radio-nuclides apart from other harmful substances is that emission of radiation may persist for very long periods. Each radio-isotope has its own characteristic *half life*, which is defined as *the time over which the radioactivity is reduced to one half of its initial value.*

The decay curve is therefore not linear, but exponential. Thus suppose a specimen of caesium–137, which has a half life of approximately 30 years, has an activity of 100 arbitrary units. After 30 years the radioactivity will have dropped to 50 units; and after another 30 years to half of 50 units, viz 25 units. It will be appreciated that the caesium–137 fallout from Chernobyl will be potentially harmful for many decades, and the contents of the Chernobyl sarcophagus for many millenia. Table XIX indicates the half lives of several radio-isotopes.

Table XIX
Half lives of certain radio-isotopes

isotope	half life
polonium–212	3×10^{-7} seconds
iodine–131	8 days
caesium–134	2·06 years
caesium–137	30 years
radium–226	1600 years
plutonium–239	24 100 years
uranium–235	$7·04 \times 10^8$ years
uranium–238	$4·5 \times 10^9$ years.

The basis of measurement of the age of carbon-containing ancient materials or artifacts relies on the proportion of carbon–14 to total carbon in the specimen or sample. At the growth of a plant or tree, naturally occurring carbon–14, with other isotopes of carbon, are assimilated. The carbon–14 (a beta-emitter) thereafter decays, its half-life being approximately 5730 years. [The value is subject to amendment]. The approximate age of the sample may therefore be determined by measuring the proportion of carbon–14 present. The method is applicable for specimens up to about 40 000 years old.

Some early workers in the field of radiation physics

Antoine Henri Becquerel (1852–1908) a French physicist, discovered radioactivity, in uranium, in 1896. He shared the 1903 Nobel Prize for Physics with Pierre (1859–1906) and Marie Curie (1867–1934), the discoverers of radium.

Louis Harold Gray (1905–1965) was an English physicist. His main work was in the measurement of ionizing radiation.

Rolf Maximilian Sievert (1896–1966) was a Swedish scientist. In the early 1920s, hospitals did not standardize the amount of radiation administered to patients. Sievert and his assistants developed the Sievert condenser chamber to measure dosage, and these were soon in use throughout the world. His later work led to his recognition as a world authority on radiological protection.

Measures of concentration of substances

Newspaper reports on pollution or contamination are usually phrased in such subjective terms as 'half the safety level', 'twice the agreed level', 'well below the acceptable limit'. Such phrases are obviously unsatisfactory. Seldom is the so-called 'safety limit' specified in terms of units, neither is the name of the authority which has laid down such a limit often mentioned. Of even more importance is the fact that in many cases various authorities specify different safety limits. Some workers in the field believe that there is no such thing as a safe limit for certain types of radiation.

One might expect, or at least hope that newspapers, radio and television would try to familiarise the general public with the names of the units used to specify levels of pollution and contamination. Actual figures could be given, so that when recommended safety levels have to be changed as a result of research or experience, the public would be able to develop a more informed opinion concerning the situation.

One measure of concentration, that of pH, is an objective description of acidity or alkalinity of solutions. See Appendix F (pp411–412) for more details. The following examples illustrate measures of concentration of contaminants or undesirables found in certain situations.

Lead in blood

For measuring the contamination of human blood by lead, a very small unit is appropriate. A person living in a rural area might be expected to have a concentration of about 10 micrograms of lead per 100 mL of blood, whilst city folk usually have about 20–30 micrograms/100 millilitres. There is serious risk of lead poisoning when the value of blood contamination reaches 80 to 100 micrograms/100 mL. In 1983 a European Community directive fixed a maximum safety level of lead in blood of 35 micrograms/100 mL. The US Centers for Disease Control (CDC) issued a statement in October 1991, revising its 1985 level of 25 micrograms/100 mL downward to 10 micrograms/100 mL.

From the late 1980s unleaded petrol has become increasingly available. In Britain by 1993 some 45% of petrol being sold was of the non-leaded varieties. In some countries (eg Canada) petrol containing lead additives may not be sold (1994). For some years past unleaded petrol only has been on general sale in the USA.

Lead in water

When specifying the amount of lead in water, the convenient values are usually in micrograms per litre. The gradual elimination of lead pipes for water supplies to domestic premises has reduced considerably the danger of brain damage and other health hazards. Since 1987, anglers in Britain's inland waters may not use lead shot fishing weights exceeding 0·05 gram. Weights are now made of less toxic metals such as zinc, tin, bismuth, or copper. At the start of the 1995 wildfowl shooting season (1 September) a so-called 'voluntary ban' on the use of lead-shot came in to force; steel, tin or bismuth-alloy shot becoming then available. The situation after this 'ban' is to be reviewed in 1997. The original limit value for lead in potable water specified by the World Health Organisation (WHO) was 100 micrograms/litre. This is now regarded as too high and a figure of 50 micrograms/litre has been specified by the EEC as an upper limit. Such limits are formally described as *prescribed concentrational values*.

Other pollutants in water

A typical permissible discharge level of effluent from a factory in the UK may have an upper limit of 20 mg/litre of BOD (the biochemical [or biological] oxygen demand). The limits for suspended solids are 30 mg/litre at 30°C.

Expressing the concentration of nitrates present in water as the nitrate radical (NO_3^-) as a whole gives a different value from when it is expressed as the nitrogen (N) on its own. Thus a concentration of 50 mg/litre as nitrate (NO_3^-) corresponds to 11·3 mg/litre as nitrogen. These figures corresponded to the original EEC limit but the World Health Organisation have now fixed the limit as 45 mg/litre as nitrate or 10 mg/litre as nitrogen.

The amount of aluminium in water supplied to the public needs to be monitored regularly. Scientists have found that the risk of Alzheimer's disease is 1·5 time higher in districts where the concentration of aluminium exceeds 100 micrograms per litre than in districts where levels are less than 10 micrograms per litre. The EEC has set an upper limit of 200 micrograms per litre for public water supply. These facts illustrate the uncertainty of the so-called 'safe limits' of contamination: this applies to all types of pollution. A careless contamination of water supplies with aluminium sulphate at Camelford, Cornwall on 6 July 1988 may enable future researchers to establish the long-term effects of acute aluminium poisoning.

Atmospheric pollutants – sulphur dioxide and carbon monoxide

This pollution comes mainly from the burning of coal and oil. Formerly, in London, for example, the average level of sulphur dioxide in the atmosphere were about 400 micrograms/m^3 but values of 1000 to 2000 in this unit have been measured for short periods. In the rare condition, popularly known as 'smog', the concentration can be as high as 6000 micrograms/m^3. According to Dr K Mellanby,[168] there is no safe 'threshold' level of atmospheric pollution by sulphur dioxide. From sources in the USA it is confirmed that a level of 500 micrograms/m^3 brings about increased hospital admission rates for elderly people with respiratory trouble.

One of the constituents of atmospheric pollution arising from the burning of coal is carbon monoxide. Vehicle exhaust gases also contribute to this pollution. A very severe case was reported in 1982 in Ankara in Turkey where the level of carbon monoxide in the city rose to the value of 141 mg/m^3, more than twice the accepted maximum of 70 milligrams per cubic metre. Mention too is made here of other aerial contaminants; ozone, nitrogen dioxide, particulates and organic compounds such as benzene and 1,3-butadiene. Car exhaust systems are increasingly fitted with catalysing units that greatly reduce emissions of carbon monoxide and oxides of nitrogen. Figure 29 shows the air quality reports that may be seen on television.

Alcohol tests for car drivers

For the breathalyser test as applied to motorists, an intermediate size of unit is used in order to give results in convenient whole numbers. In the UK the maximum permitted concentration that will obviate further police action is specified at 80 mg of alcohol (ethanol) per 100 mL of blood. This is indicated by a test on the subject's breath showing 35 micrograms of alcohol per 100 mL of exhaled air. In

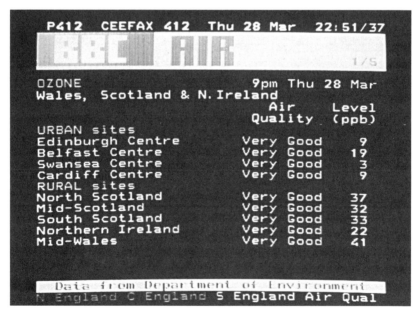

Figure 29 – Air quality report on television.

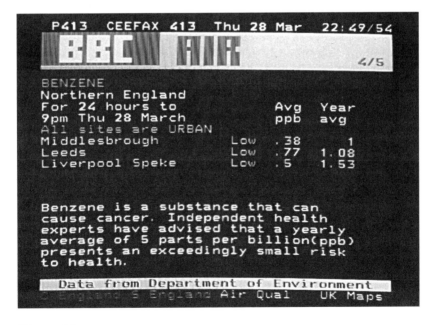

Figure 29a

other countries the maximum specified levels may be different: in mid-1996, eight European countries have a 50mg/100mL limit; whilst Poland and Sweden, 20mg/mL is the maximum. In Finland, Hungary and Romania driving with any alcohol in the blood is prohibited (*The Times*, 21 May 1996).

Mass per unit mass

Although the amount of alcohol in the blood can be measured as a true concentration, there are criteria used for some purposes which relate the intake of alcohol by an individual to the weight of his body. In some investigations relating to the slowing of brain function due to the consumption of alcohol, a mass/mass ratio was used. Values of the order of 0·5 g of alcohol per kilogram of body weight appear to produce in most persons a discernible abnormal delay between an applied stimulus and the person's response.

There was a report published in 1971 relating to the 'meals-on-wheels' service to the elderly. In this it was stated that cabbage which had 34 mg of vitamin C per 100 g when freshly cooked had in some cases as little as 3·7 mg/100 g of vitamin C when it eventually reached the pensioners.

Parts per million and milligrams per litre

The use of 'parts per million', abbreviated to ppm, is common; particularly in problems relating to pollution and contamination. The disadvantage of this terminology is that often no clue is given as to whether ppm relates to parts by volume or parts by mass. Guide-lines for a 'safe' environment put the limit of carbon monoxide in the atmosphere at 50 ppm. Over 4000 ppm of carbon monoxide in the air is deadly (less than $\frac{1}{2}$ of 1%) if breathed for any substantial time.

When data about potable water are given, values formerly specified as parts per million are now usually given as milligrams per litre (mg/L). Micrograms per litre (µg/L) are used when specifying appropriately lower concentrations or limits.

Concern has been expressed in many quarters about the increase in the amount of carbon dioxide (CO_2) in the atmosphere. The value in 1880 was about 280 ppm, 335 ppm by 1977, and by 1989 this had risen to about 350 generally, and 358 ppm in Alaska; figures that evidence a relentless rise (see Kaye & Laby[144A] – 1995 edition). Carbon dioxide is one of the main 'greenhouse gases', the effect of which may be responsible for gradual warming of the earth's climates.

Nitrates in water intended for public supply are required have concentrations of less than 11·3 parts per million, ie 11·3 mg/L.

Sausages are permitted to contain up to 450 ppm of sulphur dioxide (chemically combined) as a preservative; most brands contain much less than this and some none at all. Until the late 1970s organo-mercury compounds had been used in the control of, particularly, cereal rusts and smuts. These mycocides and their degradation products came to be recognised as dangerously persistent, and hence mercury products were phased out. The Great Lakes of the USA and Canada were particularly contaminated by the run-off. Levels of mercury in fish seem to vary widely, but are likely to progressively decline. The United States Food and Drug Administration set as a maximum for common marine food fish a value of 0·5 parts of mercury per million parts of muscle.

The amount of lead in household dust can be seen to be a fairly high value when expressed in parts per million. One survey of 38 samples of 'indoor' dust showed that the lead content was 4692 parts per million. Since about 1990, both environmental concerns and fiscal inducements have encouraged the use of lead-free petrol, and thus lead contamination is on the decline.

In some parts of the country the public water supply is fluoridated to bring the level up to 1 part per million. At this level an individual would ingest one milligram of fluoride ions from every litre (approximately 1¾ imperial pints). It is recognised that levels of fluoride above 1 ppm in drinking water can be harmful. Such a high level would produce mottled teeth in children after prolonged drinking of this water. Where naturally-occuring fluorides were high (eg parts of Sunderland and Maldon, Essex up until the 1950s); darkish, mottled, though strong and decay-resistant teeth, were commonly seen.

Toxic metals are sometimes found in food itself, and in certain drinks. In the UK the maximum statutory limit for lead in most food before cooking is 2 ppm; up to 5 ppm is permitted in tinned meats. For tinned baby-foods the maximum lead content is 0·5 ppm, ie 0·5 mg lead per kilogram.

Certain authorities including the UK's Ministry of Agriculture are setting 'official' Tolerable Daily Intakes (TDIs) for certain contaminating chemicals, eg phthalates in some brands of formula milk (*Independent on Sunday*, 26 May 1996).

It must be admitted (in 1996) that the designation of concentration 'parts per billion' (ppb), signifying parts per thousand million is in such common use as to be secure. Aerial pollutants; nitrogen dioxide, benzene, ozone, carbon monoxide; are monitored daily and reports of concentration displayed on the British television data pages Teletext and Ceefax: see Figure 29, pages 264–5. Where appropriate, laboratories where potable water is tested specify the results of their analyses in mg/L or µg/L.

Pressure

Pressure is not a quantity encountered very frequently outside industry; though two cases familiar to the general public are motor car tyre pressure and atmospheric pressure.

The pascal (Pa) was adopted by the 14th CGPM which met in Paris in October 1971. It is the derived SI unit of pressure and is equal to 1 N/m^2. With the official SI range of prefixes it is capable of covering the full range of pressures met with in practice. These range from about 10^{-12} torr to about 10^4 atmospheres. Thus 1 Pa = $0·75 \times 10^{-8}$ torr (ultra-high vacuum) and 1 GPa = 14 504 lbf/in^2, and only a few cases would arise outside these limits.

On the Continent of Europe, motor car tyre pressures have usually been expressed in kgf/cm^2. The bar is only 2% greater than the kgf/cm^2. Since the bar is a unit permissible under CGPM rules its use for tyre pressure is acceptable. A good idea of the chaos that has existed in pressure units can be obtained from Appendix B7. Table XX shows some typical values of tyre pressures.

		Table XX		
Equivalent values of tyre pressures				
lbf/in^2	20	24	28	32
kgf/cm^2	1·41	1·69	1·97	2·25
bar	1·38	1·65	1·93	2·21
kPa	138	165	193	221

If the word 'bar' seems an unusual one to lay-persons, they need only remember that it is related to barometer or barometric pressure; 1·7 bar, for example, means a pressure above atmospheric pressure equal to 1·7 times the average value of atmospheric pressure at sea level.

In practice much use is made of the SI prefix milli, in order to avoid decimal points; in weather reports the millibar is generally used.

In the weather forecast for shipping, broadcast by the BBC on Radio 4, there are two numbers, the identity and dimensions of which are not stated. The first of these can be easily recognised because it relates to the direction and strength of the wind in a particular area. An example of this would be 'South-West 3' which would mean a wind from the south-west of force 3 on the Beaufort Scale (Appendix D1 p395ff). The second figure, which is not much above or below 1000, gives the atmospheric pressure in millibars. Frequently the statement is made that this pressure is changing; examples might be '980, falling slowly' and '1015, rising slowly'.

Extremely low values of pressure are symptomatic of very bad weather. The worst case of this in recent times in the UK was the hurricane which swept through the South of England on 15/16 October 1987. The barometric pressure had fallen to the extremely low value of 958 millibars. This storm resulted in 30 deaths and the destruction of some 15 million trees. There had been an even lower value of barometric pressure in 1982 when the London Weather Centre recorded a value of 932 millibars.

In a typhoon in the South Pacific occurred the lowest ever recorded value of atmospheric pressure at sea level equal to 877 millibars, though there is some doubt as to the accuracy of the report. Around the UK a barometric pressure of about 1040 mb would be high. Elsewhere, a figure of 1084 mb has been recorded.

The normal type of household barometer in the UK has a scale marked in inches of mercury, the highest reading being usually 31 inches and the lowest 26 inches. To convert readings in inches of mercury to millibars the relationship 1000 mb = 29·531 inches of mercury can be used. Suggestions have been made that the hectopascal should replace the millibar.

It has been found convenient for scientific purposes to define a standard value of atmospheric pressure, called a standard atmosphere. The defined physical atmosphere is equal to 101 325 N/m^2 = 1·013 25 bar = 1 013 250 dyn/cm^2 (all exact values), which in imperial measure is equal to 14·695 9 lbf/in^2 approximately. This definition of the standard atmosphere was made by the CGPM in 1954 and remains unaltered by the introduction of SI.

Illumination

The SI unit – the candela – is suitable only for describing the magnitude of emitted light from a source. Various derived units are necessary to properly evaluate or quantify and so describe the effects of a light. Not least must be considered the distance from the light and the characteristics of the illuminated artifact. These are some of the matters considered in the following sections.

Power of a light source

In that branch of technology called illumination engineering, the base unit is that which designates the luminous intensity of a source of light. Originally this unit was called the 'candle-power'.

The first attempt to reduce the chaos in standards of luminous intensity existing early in the 20th century was made in 1909. By an agreement between the USA, France and the UK an 'international candle' was set up as a standard. This was maintained by electric lamps. As late as 1936 it was admitted that the international candle differed in magnitude in different countries.

Studies were developed in the 1920s for an entirely new type of primary light source as a standard. It was proposed to define a unit based on the light emitted from a square centimetre of molten platinum at its solidifying point [1768°C]. In 1937 the new proposed standard seemed ready for adoption but the advent of the Second World War (1939–1945) caused the decision on this proposal to be postponed. In 1948 the 9th CGPM ratified the new unit and gave it the name 'candela' (symbol cd). The accuracy in the magnitude of the candela based on this process was not much better than 1%, which is crude compared with that of the other base unit standards.

A new definition of the candela was introduced in 1979: this definition is given in Appendix A1.

Luminous flux

From the base unit of luminous intensity, the candela, one obtains the first derived unit, that of luminous flux in the following manner. A point source of light having a luminous intensity of one candela, uniform in all direction, is placed at the centre of a sphere which has a radius of one metre, another SI unit of course. Each square metre of surface area subtends at the centre a solid angle of one steradian. The luminous flux emitted in any one such solid angle is defined as 1 lumen (symbol lm). Since there are 4π steradians subtended by a complete sphere, it follows that a point source of light of intensity 1 cd produces a total luminous flux of 4π lumens.

Light output related to power input

Comparison between different types of light source is best made in terms of the light flux in lumens per unit of input power to the lamp. The following notes give some idea of the spectacular increase in efficacy of electrical sources of light.

In considering the figures given below, one must bear in mind the fact that the accuracy of the measured values of light output in the early days was of a very low order. In addition, the magnitude of the units candlepower and lumen do not correspond exactly to current units. However, the impovement in the output of light from electrical sources has been so great that these discrepancies can be considered to be marginal and hence not to distort the general picture. The power input that is not emitted as light does, of course, appear as heat: to be expected in accordance with the principle of the conservation of energy.

Prior to the First World War (1914–1918) the efficacy of electric light sources improved as shown in Table XXI.

Table XXI		
Efficacies of various filament lamps		
type of filament lamp	*date in use commercially*	*output in lumens per watt*
carbon	1896	3·3
tantalum	1905	6
tungsten (vacuum type)	1908	8
tungsten (gas-filled type)	1913	12

The range of frequencies of light detected by the human eye extends from about 4000 Å to about 7000 Å, or in SI units from 400 nm to 700 nm. At very high intensities, an even wider frequency-range is discernible. The peak response of the human eye to light of the various visible wavelengths is in the vicinity of 555 nm, that is, in the yellow/green part of the spectrum.

Gas discharge lamps of the neon type were first made in 1907 but were not suitable for general illumination. Neon lamps were cold-cathode tubes, and hot-cathode tubes were not developed until the 1930s, culminating in the fluorescent tubes of 1937 with an efficacy of about 35 lm/W. Continuous development has brought this figure in 1994 up to over 70 lm/W.

Illuminance

When some of the luminous flux from a lamp falls on a surface we specify the illumination of that surface in terms of the number of lumens falling on one square metre of that surface. The unit of illuminance is one lumen per square metre and is called the lux, symbol lx.

For ease of comparison all the figures available from earlier sources have been converted to lux. Common values of illumination indoors during the first 25 years of the 20th century tended to be in the range of 30 to 50 lux, with 75 to 100 lux for fine work.

The following figures relating to artificial illumination are representative of good modern practice. No working space should have an illuminance of less than 200 lux on the working plane; the recommended value at the part of the working surface where ordinary work is being done is 400 lux. For partially-sighted people an illuminance of about 1600 lux is required, usually obtained over a relatively small area such as by a table lamp. In a particular carpet inspection and matching room the illuminance on the working surface is 3000 lux.

Natural light sources vary over a very wide range. The illumination produced on the earth's surface at the zenith by a star of the first magnitude is of the order 0·9 microlux. Bright moonlight produces an illumination on the earth of less than 0·5 lux. The average illumination out-of-doors on a dull day is about 5000 lux, and in strong sunlight can be as high as 100 000 lux.

Irradiance

The total radiation falling on an area is called irradiance. This radiation may include wavelengths throughout any part of the electromagnetic spectrum. Such radiation is measured in watts per square metre. Whatever irradiance that falls on a surface may be absorbed and involved in some electron excitation or transfer or, of course, reflected. Any radiation re-radiated (apart from that reflected) is always of a longer wavelength (and hence of lower energy) than the exciting radiation.

Emissivity

This characteristic of a material or an object is the ratio of the energy per unit area radiated by the artifact's surface to that radiated by a *black body* at the same temperature. Precise work distinguishes between total emissivity (ε_t) and spectral emissivity (ε_λ). Instruments for measurements of ε_λ are radiation pyrometers which, subject to calibration, are used as a basis for measurement of temperatures of objects in kilns and ovens.

Items made of carborundum or graphite have spectral emissivities of about 0·9, rusty iron 0·7, titanium (oxidised or not) 0·5, oxidised aluminium 0·3 and untarnished silver 0·05. Perfect reflectors would have an emissivity of 0. Emissivities are ratios; dimensionless values that must be determined by experiment. For other examples of dimensionless values see Appendix D5, p403.

Luminance

What was formerly called the 'brightness' of a light source, is now officially called the luminance. Since most light sources used in practice are relatively small in terms of surface area, the unit of luminance met with in the past has been the c.g.s. unit called the stilb (abbreviation sb), equal to 1 candela per square centimetre of emitting surface. The corresponding SI unit is the nit (abbreviation nt), equal to a luminance of 1 candela per square metre. Thus 1 sb = 10^4 nt. A rough idea of order of magnitude of the main units used in connection with luminance is given in Table XXII.

Table XXII

Approximate magnitudes of various light sources

luminance	c.g.s.	SI
minimum detectable by the human eye	0·1 nsb	1 nt
overcast sky (daylight)	0·2 sb	2000 nt
bright moon	0·5 sb	5000 nt
clear sky (daylight)	0·8 sb	8000 nt
snow in bright sunlight	1·0 sb	10 knt
100 watt pearl lamp	14·6 sb	146 knt
carbon arc crater	16 ksb	160 Mnt
sun	166 ksb	1·66 Gnt

Chapter VII Part 1

Metrication in the United Kingdom – 1838 to 1939

Early steps: the Decimal Association

In the United Kingdom efforts were made throughout the 19th century to introduce the metric system for use in industry and commerce. One of the pressure groups helping towards this end was The Decimal Association. This body was formed at a meeting of mainly businessmen in the London Tavern in Bishopsgate Street on 12 June 1854. The immediate objective of the new organisation was the introduction of decimal coinage. At this time the metric system of weights and measures was often called 'the decimal system'. In his inaugural speech the Chairman of the Decimal Association said, *inter alia*, that Sir John Wrottesley had first brought the subject of a decimal system to the attention of Parliament on 25 February 1824.

In May 1838 the Chancellor of the Exchequer Mr Spring Rice (later Lord Monteagle) secured the appointment of a Royal Commission to enquire into a possible decimal system of weights and measures. This reported in 1841 to the effect that this was impracticable without the prior introduction of decimal coinage. A further Commisssion in 1843 was set up which reported in 1853 advocating decimal coinage; with a pound (sterling) divided into 1000 parts, the proposed sub-divisions being called the florin, the cent and the mil.

A petition was drawn up by the Decimal Association for presentation to Parliament, backed by an impressive array of signatures. These included those of Richard Cobden, Joseph Whitworth, Baron Lionel Rothschild; and James Simpson, who was then President of the Institution of Civil Engineers. In addition to the support of 52 'Lord Mayors and the like', there were on the petition the names of 13 'Scientific and Literary Institutions'. These were hardly the most prominent in the land; one was the Preston Institution for Diffusion of Useful Information, and seven of them were Mechanics Institutions. Many years later the Preston Organisation became a highly regarded College called the Harris Institute and later still the University of Central Lancashire. Many mechanics institutions became technical colleges of high repute. In case some of the Members of Parliament who were to receive the petition were not clear as to the meaning of the word 'decimal', this was defined in the preface to the Petition as follows: 'of or relating to ten; if there were a pure English word answering to it, we should have "tennish" or "tenly"'.

On Tuesday, 20 June 1854 a deputation from The Decimal Association met Mr Gladstone, the Chancellor of the Exchequer, to advocate the decimalisation of the coinage. Amongst other matters, the advocates stated that the resultant inconvenience 'would not be greater than that which in Ireland attended the assimiliation of the currency of that country with the currency of this, when the shilling of 12 pence was substituted for that of 13 pence'. The gist of Mr Gladstone's reply to the petitioners was that public opinion was not ripe for the proposed change.

It is interesting to note that the Irish currency change did not, in fact, take place in the manner intended by Parliament. The idea behind the legislation of 1826 was that 13 Irish pennies should be exchanged for 12 new Irish pennies, but unfortunately the Mint was not fully prepared for the change. In the event what happened was that a proclamation had to be issued declaring the Irish copper coins legal tender in the United Kingdom at the English copper value. This meant that the value of the Irish penny was raised gratuitously by just over 8% of its original value.

Moves towards legislation

From 1862 onwards efforts were not lacking in Parliament to change the legal system of weights and measures from imperial to metric. The story, however, is mainly one of lost opportunities. It illustrates quite clearly the limitations of Members of Parliament when confronted by a decision to be made at variance with Ministerial policy, which usually tends to be held back even in the face of unprecedented inertia for change.

When the metric system had first been adopted in late 18th century France the indifference and even hostility towards it in the UK was quite understandable; for a long time Britain and France were either at war with each other or in a state of mutual distrust. The rapid development of science was probably the initial source of the impetus to consider seriously the use of the metric system; to a less extent commercial considerations arising from the export trade played some part in weakening the adherence in the UK to imperial units.

In the House of Commons on 18 February 1864 was taken the First Reading of a Private Member's Bill, the object of which was 'to render permissive the use of the Metric System of Weights and Measures in this country'. On the occasion of the Second Reading (9 March 1864) Mr W Ewart (Member for Dumfries) said that the Bill which he had introduced in 1863 was based on the unanimous report of a Committee of the House, except that it had envisaged a compulsory change to the metric system. The present measure, he said, was permissive only; he believed that the metric system even if only permissive 'would work its way gradually into the commerce and manufactures of the country, until at last the people would become convinced that it was desirable to pass a compulsory measure'. Opponents of the Bill disliked its 'foreignness': the 'labouring man' would still want his pint, and 'English measures' could be decimalised; but without decimal coinage that would make things worse. On its Second Reading, the Bill was approved by 90 votes to 52. At the Third Reading of the Bill on 4 May 1864 Mr Thomas Milner Gibson, President of the Board of Trade, expressed his opposition on the grounds that it seemed to call for a new material standard (for the metre), but he agreed with the limited purpose of metric units being recognised as legal in contracts. Since the sponsors of the Bill had declared that 'the legalization of contracts in this country under the metric system was the pith of the Bill', it was finally passed into law in this restricted form.

Two years later, a rather wider Bill was passed by Congress in the USA authorising the use in that country of the metric system of weights and measures, but this also was permissive and not compulsory.

It is hardly exaggerating to say that the Act of 1864 failed completely as far as the commercial use of the metric system in the UK was concerned. A question being asked in the House of Commons by Mr J B Smith on 16 April 1869 revealed that a person had been summoned before the Magistrates for having in his possession metric weights and measures. This action had been taken as a result of a circular that had been issued by the Standards Department of the Board of Trade dated 19 April 1867, addressed to Inspectors of Weights and Measures throughout the Country. The circular stated that 'upon a case submitted to the Law Officers of the Crown upon the legal construction of *The Metric Weights and Measures Act 1864*, they have given an opinion that a person using Metrical Weights and Measures is liable to have them seized, and to conviction and forfeiture of the weights under the Act 5 and 6 William IV c 63'. Mr Smith asked the President of the Board of Trade (the famous John Bright) whether or not he considered this to be a satisfactory state of the law. The reply was 'The state of the law is not satisfactory – for nothing could be more absurd than that a man having in his possession a certain description of weights and measures, should be liable to have them seized, although the law intended that he should use them. I am only surprised that my Honourable Friend did not take care when the Bill was passing that it was more carefully worded'. He then continued in words that echo frequently in the House with variations in phrasing: '. . . sometime, when the Government or the Board of Trade has a great deal more leisure than at present, possibly a measure on the subject may be introduced'. The Government of this day is still short of time for business, and it seems likely that future Governments will suffer similarly!

In 1895 a Select Committee of the House recommended:

(a) That the metrical system of weights and measures be at once legalised for all purposes.

(b) That after a lapse of 2 years the metrical system be rendered compulsory by Act of Parliament.

(c) That the metrical system of weights and measures be taught in all public elementary schools as a necessary and integral part of arithmetic, and that decimals be introduced at an earlier period of the school curriculum than is the case at present.

The early years of the 20th century

Strenuous efforts were made by widely different sections of the
community to make an advance on the 1897 result, by introducing a
compulsory change to the metric system in the United Kingdom.

A curious situation arose in Parliament during the year 1904. A
Government measure was presented to the Commons, the main object
of which was to tidy up certain aspects of general weights and measures
practice, particularly in relation to the lack of uniformity in local
administration. Thus, for example, individual dead weights used by a
trader and certified as correct in value by one local authority might
not be acceptable to another local authority.

Thus the 1904 Act provided for the periodical verification and
stamping of weights, measures and weighing instruments in a prescribed
manner. There was, however, in the fourth and last part of the Bill
a proposal that, from January 1908, Troy and apothercaries weight
should be abolished and metric weight introduced for this restricted
range of application. Although this proposed change would be hardly
perceptible to the general public, the majority of the Members present
regarded this as the thin edge of the wedge which might lead to further
metrication, and the movers and seconders of the Bill were forced to
withdraw this particular section of the Bill, whereupon the major
legislation was passed with ease.

Whilst all this was proceeding in the House of Commons, there
was before the House of Lords a Private Member's Bill of potentially
greater importance. It was presented for First Reading by Lord Kelvin
on 2 February 1904. This Bill proposed to render compulsory the
use of the metric system of weights and measures in the UK at an
early date. Petitions had been received from all parts of the country
in favour of this radical change. Altogether some 8 million people
had signed petitions; sponsored by such widely different organisations
as city and town councils, trades unions, inspectors of weights
and measures, teachers' associations and chambers of commerce.
These were presented at the Second Reading of the Bill of 23 February
1904. Lord Belhaven and Stenton, moving the Second Reading,

pointed out that the Act of 1897 did not satisfy the second recommendation of the Select Committee of 1895; namely, that after two years from the consent of Parliament the use of the metric system should be made compulsory in the UK. A conference of all the Premiers of the Self-Governing Colonies had passed a resolution in 1902, urging the adoption of the metric system throughout the British Empire. Lord Belhaven pointed out that in the USA a Bill was before Congress proposing to change to metric units in that country as from 1 January 1906. This last statement would not in 1904 have been as powerful an argument as it would be today. The relative economic positions of the UK and the USA at that time were not what they are now (1996) and it is more than likely that had the UK given the lead in this matter in 1904, it would have been followed by the USA.

A curious fact mentioned by Lord Belhaven was that milk from Buckinghamshire was still being sent to London and sold by the 'barn gallon'. This unit, now obsolete, was equal to 2 UK gallons or 2·4 USA gallons. For some obscure reason he suggested that the spelling of the metre be changed to meter, and litre to liter, as per the practice in the United States.

Lord Colchester stated that at that time 45% of our export trade was with metric countries and 55% with non-metric countries. Lord Kelvin pointed out that Germany had become fully metric two years previously. In answer to those who seemed to object to the 'foreigness' of the metric system, he stated that 'the decimal system, worked out by French philosophers, originated in England. In a letter dated 14 November 1783, James Watt laid down a plan which was in all respects the system adopted by the French philosophers seven years later'. The word 'philosopher' might seem curious in this context, but it should be remembered that Kelvin had been appointed in 1846 a Glasgow University 'Professor of Natural Philosophy', which in English University terms would have denoted a Professor of Physics. Kelvin then went on to describe a narrow escape from death he had had during an experiment involving explosives. He had weighed out the amount of explosive in units of apothecaries weight instead of avoirdupois measure, giving approximately twice the safe amount of explosive. Thinking that the amount seemed rather large, he looked up the matter in a reference book and discovered the mistake just in time to prevent his being badly or fatally injured.

Mr Balfour's Government was of the opinion that the proposed period of two years before compulsion came in was too short. The Bill never got to the Commons in that session, the Government insisting on the setting up of a Select Committee before it would agree to consider supporting the measure.

The 1907 Parliamentary Bill

It was 1907 before the next attempt at mandatory metrication was made in Parliament. A Bill 'To render compulsory the use of the system of Weights and Measures commonly known as the Metric System' received its First Reading on 15 February. The Second Reading was taken on 22 March, introduced as a Private Member's Bill by Mr B S Strauss (Member for Tower Hamlets, Mile End). He said *inter alia*, 'Some people said – and with a certain amount of truth – that there was prejudice against the metric system on account of its foreign origin; its originator was one of the greatest Englishmen (sic) this country ever produced – James Watt.' He was a Scot.

Strauss then went on to point out that a seam of glass was 120 lb; a seam of straw in Devon equalled 200 lb; a seam of hay in the same county was 373 lb. He asked the House to note the figure 373; it was a prime number and hence not divisible by any other existing whole number. He asked why there should be 24¾ cubic feet in the solid perch of mason's work, and only 12⅜ cubic feet if it was brickwork. He cited the absurd position arising from the fact that although a stone as a unit of weight was normally regarded as equal to 14 lb, a stone of glass weighed 5 lb, a stone of meat 8 lb, a stone of cheese 16 lb and a stone of hemp 32 lb. After recalling the experience of Lord Kelvin as related by him in the 1904 debate, Strauss returned to the lack of uniformity in what was meant by various measures in the imperial system. Thus in Worcestershire a pot was equal to 4 pecks whilst in other counties a pot varied from 64 lb to 94 lb. A bushel of potatoes in Cornwall was 224 lb but in Nottingham 84 lb. He cited 'an eminent French schoolmaster' who had stated that their system of weights and measures could be taught in 20 hours, but it took 400 hours to get an idea of the 'English antiquated system'. In the 1904 Bill a period of two years had been envisaged as the transitional period from imperial to metric: in this Bill a period of three years was being proposed.

Seconding the Bill, Sir H Norman (Member for Wolverhampton) produced for inspection 'a little bit of metal . . . a steel rule which Lord Kelvin had described as the key to the metric system'. He said that a boy of nine years of age had completely grasped the principles behind it in ten minutes. The rule was 1 mm thick, 1 cm wide and 10 cm long; ten of them placed end to end would make a metre; 1000 metres would make a kilometre. From the cubes of the linear measures were derived the measure of capacity and weight . . .'. He then mentioned those opponents of the Bill who said that one could have a decimal system without it being metric. He said that Thomas Parker (founder of The Electric Construction Company of Wolverhampton) had 'invented a system called the decimal inch'!

An opponent of the Bill, an MP who was the head of a famous engineering firm, had said to him, 'Your Bill would render useless all my patterns, templets (sic) metals and gauges going back over half a century'. Norman's reply to that was that if those patterns, etc, went back half a century it was probably high time many of them were scrapped! He then went on to deal with another objection being put forward to the Bill. It was said that in France, the home of the decimal system (sic), the old-fashioned measures were largely in use. This was not true, he replied, since although some of the old-fashioned names were still being used, the actual units were now metric.

The Lancashire Textile Industry seemed to be the source of the main opposition to the new measure. Mr Haworth (Manchester, South) began by stating that the pressure group behind the Bill was the 'Decimal Association' and yet it was not proposed to decimalise the coinage. He said that the estimated cost of the change to metric for the Engineering Industry was about £100 000 000. When he was questioned about this figure it emerged that this estimate had been quoted by the said Thomas Parker, but that when challenged by Lord Kelvin, he had withdrawn it at once and admitted that 'he had no authority for it'. Mr Haworth then admitted that 'a hopeless mistake

had been made', but he continued to bandy about figures ranging from
£200 000 to £50 000 000, the former value being quoted by an American; and the latter, pure supposition! He said there were 750 000
looms in Lancashire and one manufacturer had quoted 30 shillings
per loom to make the necessary alterations. Then followed a most
peculiar argument. He said that *any* change would do harm to our
export trade; and mentioned that, for example, goods exported to China
had for years been marked with a stamp which was upside down, and
the goods were rejected when this was discovered, and the mark
imprinted the right way up! At that time Lancashire was exporting
over 6000 million yards of cloth per annum, valued at 75 million
pounds sterling. When it was pointed out that Clause 3 Section (c) of
the Bill gave His Majesty, by Order in Council, power to exempt
from the requirements of the Bill any calling or industry which so
desired, the MPs representing textile constituencies maintained their
opposition, pointing out that the uniformity claimed to result from the
operation of the Bill would vanish.

Once again that 'sacred cow' of 'the people', the pint of beer, came
into the debate. Sir George Scott Robertson (Member for Bradford,
Central) said, 'It was once said by a President of the Board of Trade
that the strongest Government in this country could not change the
measure of the pint'. Again there was a complete misconception as
to the position in the United States. Mr Kelley (Manchester, South-
West) said that 'As the Americans were about to adopt the metric
system it might be a means of causing the matter to be taken up in
the United States and might lead in the desired direction'.

As a Private Member's Bill taken on a Friday afternoon, it had
little chance of being carried against the disinterest of the Government
of the day. David Lloyd George, then President of the Board of Trade,
opposed the Bill. Other prominent members voting against the Bill
were Herbert Henry Asquith (then Chancellor of the Exchequer),
J Austin Chamberlain, Rufus Daniel Isaacs, Walter Runciman, and
the notorious Horatio Bottomly! The voting was 118 for the Bill, 150
against, giving of majority of 32.

The rejection of the Bill was a triumph for a pressure group called
the British Weights and Measures Association, which had been formed
in 1904 'for the purpose of defending and, where practicable, improving

the present system of British Weights and Measures'. Amongst the more prominent of the supporters of this Association were Robert Kaye Gray, a past President of the Institution of Electrical Engineers; Archibald Denny, a ship-builder; J H Wickstead, a past President of the Institution of Mechanical Engineers; and Thomas Parker of Wolverhampton. Incidentally, it was he who designed and constructed that electrical work for the original and still-existing tramway (1996) in England, the Blackpool-Fleetwood tramway; a mode of transport recently reintroduced in Manchester and Sheffield.

Renewed efforts to introduce metrication

As indicated, after the failure of the effort made in 1907 to make compulsory the use of the metric system in the UK, there was a long period of relative quiescence. A pressure group called The Decimal Association had been formed as far back as 1854, the main purpose of which was to bring about decimalisation of the coinage in the UK. In the *News Bulletin of the Decimal Association* for 1937–38 there were reported to be strong feelings amongst the members that a change to the metric system should be the main plank in their platform. The Council Members, whilst in agreement with metrication as an objective, felt that this could only come about after decimalisation of the coinage. Slight progress was reported in their secondary objective of metrication in that the Ordinance Survey Office in Southampton had started to prepare an 'International Local Aeronautical Map' with metric scales. It had also recommended that when a National Grid was designed for their maps, this should employ metric dimensions.

Other items from the reports of the Decimal Association about this time were as follows. Germany was reported to be on the verge of introducing the 'grade' system of angles, that is, the use of decimal sub-divisions for angle measurement instead of the sexagesimal system of sub-division. It was reported from then onwards that foreign currency exchange figures would henceforth be quoted in decimals; the 'familiar figures $4·92½ for £1 sterling' were a 'shocking example of what not to do'. In 1939 an estimate was made by Reverend A J Stubbs concerning the financial gain that would result in the sphere of education from the adoption of decimal coinage and the exclusive use of the metric system in the UK. This saving he estimated at £5 000 000 per annum. Another item from the 1939 *News Bulletin of the Decimal Association* pointed out the absurd position regarding the unit called the barrel. The position then was as follows:

One barrel could mean

200 lb beef	4 firkins (224 lb) butter	168 lb saltpetre
224 lb pork	26¼ gallons of tar	100 lb gunpowder
500 herrings	36 gallons of beer	14 stone of oats.

A peculiar feature of the propaganda put out by the Decimal Association was to advocate the use of the American spellings liter for litre and meter for metre.

But the year 1939, with the clouds of war gathering, was a dark time for the United Kingdom. Inertia for change was frustrated for a decade or more. The commoner, soldier, sailor, airman, politician and the rest; all had other and more pressing matters than the adoption of metric units to concentrate the mind.

Chapter VII Part 2

Metrication in the United Kingdom – 1939 to 1972

Introduction

There was little opportunity for debate, nor possibility of progress in the adoption of metrication in the late 1930s and the 1940s. Most countries in Europe and much of the rest of the world were engaged in a debilitating war against Germany, Italy and Japan. Even after the end of hostilities in 1945, some years slid by whilst rebuilding and production got under way. In the 20th century, a century that saw the evolution of powered flight, men walking on the moon and the development of microprocessors of undreamed-of computing power, the distressing interlude of the Second World War (1939–1945) and its aftermath were both a drain for stagnation, and a force for change – political and social, rather than for the adoption of a novel system of weights and measures.

Another monolith that undoubtedly influenced the rate of change was the 'Cold War'; that ideological struggle principally between the United States of America and its allies on the one part, and the United Soviet Socialist Republics together with its Eastern European satellites; lasting from 1945 through to the early 1990s. This also probably proved a hindrance to metrication. It is little wonder that in a century of progress, there was but a slow crawl along the road towards metrication in the United Kingdom.

1951: The Hodgson Report

On 11 May 1951 there was presented to Parliament the *Report of the Committee on Weights and Measures Legislation* Cmd 8219, subsequently referred to as *The Hodgson Report*.[171] This proved to be a very thorough examination of the effects of the law relating to weights and measures upon traders and upon the public generally in the UK. Early in the report it was pointed out that it was 'hardly correct to talk of the "imperial system" of weights and measures in quite the same way say as one talks of the "metric system". The latter forms one compact, closely-defined and universally recognised system of measurement under the guidance of an international body . . . whereas the imperial system is really a conglomeration of units . . . which have been linked together to form a rough whole'. The report goes on to state 'The real problem facing Great Britain . . . is not whether to adhere either to the imperial or to the metric system, but whether to maintain . . . two legal systems of measurement or to establish world-wide uniformity by changing over completely to the metric system and abolishing the imperial'. After consideration of the evidence from widely different sources relating to industrial, commercial, and educational practice, the report states that the members of the committee 'have come to the unanimous conclusion that the metric system is . . . a better system of weights and measures than the imperial; that a change from imperial to metric for all trade purposes is sooner or later inevitable. We therefore recommend that the Government should straightaway take the steps which we outline below with a view to abolishing within a definite period all use of the imperial system in Great Britain and to establishing the sole use of the metric system for all trade purposes'.

There were, however, two reservations made concerning this recommendation. One was that decimal coinage should first be introduced in the UK; this was done in 1971 with surprisingly little difficulty. The other reservation was that the change should be brought about 'in concert with those countries of North America and the Commonwealth which base their units on the yard and the pound'. The Countries of the Commonwealth soon adopted metrication; the USA in 1996 had still not done so. For a fuller discussion on this matter, see Chapter VIII.

The steps to be taken by the Government, as recommended in the report, to bring about the change to the metric system in the UK were as follows:

(a) discussion with industry and commerce to determine the period of transition;

(b) agreement with the Commonwealth and the USA for simultaneous change on their parts;

(c) a lengthy process of preparing the general public for the change;

(d) the decimalisation of the coinage;

(e) the preparation of schemes for the compulsory change-over, trade by trade, during the period of transition, with provision for compensation wherever necessary.

Except for (b) the steps recommended were taken, but only after long delays; with regard to (b) it was somewhat unrealistic to think that this step lay within the powers of the Government of the UK, and in addition the word 'simultaneous' is hardly compatible with the 'trade by trade' wording of (e).

The long delay in implementing any part of the above recommendations was understandable at the time. Britain was only just getting on its feet after the Second World War and the financial position of the Country was not very healthy. On the eve of the presentation of the report to Parliament the then President of the Board of Trade stated that the Government would not accept, at least for immediate implementation, the recommendation which was numbered 2 in the report. This stated specifically that the imperial system of measurement should be abolished in favour of the complete adoption of the metric system over a period of about 20 years.

There was less excuse, however, for the refusal of the Government to adopt the recommendation numbered 3 in the report. This stated that, whether or not the metric system was adopted, the imperial yard should be defined as 0·9144 of the international metre exactly, and the imperial pound should also be made a definite fraction (to be defined later) of the international kilogram. Such action should be made in unison with the United States Government to secure identical values in both countries. Not only were there slight discrepancies between the values of the UK and USA units but the committee had pointed out that the etalon or material standard known as the imperial standard yard compared unfavourably in both workmanship and material with the international prototype metre, and also with the British copy of the metre etalon. The imperial standard pound as an etalon also compared unfavourably with the international prototype kilogram in both workmanship and material. The legal position with regard to both the yard and the pound was unsound. All these unsatisfactory features could be put right by basing the British standards on the international metric standards, as had already been done in the USA.

The National Standards laboratories of the USA and of the UK and of four other countries (all in the British Commonwealth) decided to adopt the following exact relationships as from 1 July 1959:

1 yard = 0·9144 metre
1 pound = 0·453 592 37 kilogram.

This unified the four differing standard yards used in these countries and the three differing pounds. The figure for the pound is divisible by 7 to facilitate conversion of grains to grams, giving 1 grain = 0·064 798 91 gram. The value is identical with the international value proposed in 1959, and to all intents and purposes is the mean between the previous USA pound of 0·453 592 4277 kg and the imperial standard pound of 1878 equal to 0·453 592 338 kg. In the UK, however, the Board of Trade found it necessary to point out that these internationally agreed values of the yard and the pound had no statutory force in the UK and could not be used for trade or commerce where the values laid down by the *Weights and Measures Act 1878* must be adhered to.

This situation lasted until the passing of the *Weights and Measures Act 1963* which made legal the above exact values based on the metre and the kilogram.

For over ten years it looked as if nothing would happen concerning the most important recommendations of the Hodgson Report. The first really important moves were made by the British Standards Institute and by the Federation of British Industries, and from their initiatives has come the important development leading up to the present position of the process of metrication in the UK. In studying the following outline of the sequence of the events the public nature of the various moves should be noted, since later on certain pressure groups hostile to metrication seemed to imply in their statements that the whole process had been allowed to develop in some underhand way and without the knowledge and consent of Parliament.

Introduction of decimal currency in the UK

As early as 1957 The Confederation of British Industries had carried out a limited enquiry relating to decimalisation of the currency and metrication of weights and measures. The questions put to the 200 trade associations invited them to give their views as to whether or not it was worth while proceeding with a fresh enquiry into these two matters. There were 115 replies, and strong interest was expressed by those associations in going further with the matter.

A development which was to have a bearing on the prospects of metrication was the decision by the Government in December 1961 to set up a Committee of Inquiry on Decimal Currency under the chairmanship of the Earl of Halsbury. This committee was not asked to advise the Government as to whether or not decimalisation of the coinage was desirable, but to advise on the best method of going about it when decided upon.

The Halsbury Report was published in September 1963. It recommended that the system to be adopted should be that based on the pound sterling as the unit of currency, with 100 sub-divisions (new pennies) for the coinage, and a half of one (new penny) should be the smallest coin for the time being, its ultimate extinction due to inflation being calmly envisaged! On 1 March 1966 the Chancellor of the Exchequer announced in the House of Commons the Government's decision to enact a change to decimal currency in February 1971.[160] The Decimal Currency Bills of 1967 and 1969 were duly introduced, and passed into law.

Decimal Currency Act 1967

1967 CHAPTER 47

An Act to provide for the introduction of a decimal currency in the year 1971; and to regulate the constitution and functions of the Decimal Currency Board.   [14th July 1967]

BE IT ENACTED by the Queen's most Excellent Majesty, by and with the advice and consent of the Lords Spiritual and Temporal, and Commons, in this present Parliament assembled, and by the authority of the same, as follows:—

Currency and coinage

1.—(1) On and after the appointed day the denominations of money in the currency of the United Kingdom shall be the pound sterling and the new penny, the new penny being one-hundredth part of a pound sterling. *The new decimal currency.*

(2) In this Act " the appointed day " means such day in the year 1971 as the Treasury may by order made by statutory instrument appoint.

2.—(1) Subject to subsection (2) below, all coins of the new currency to be made at the Mint, being coins of the metals and denominations described in column 1 of Schedule 1 to this Act, shall be circular and of the standard weight, diameter and composition specified in columns 2, 3 and 4 of that Schedule. *Coinage of the new currency.*

(2) In the making of such coins a remedy (that is, a variation from the standard weight, diameter or composition specified as aforesaid) shall be allowed of an amount not exceeding the following, that is to say—

    (a) a variation from the said standard weight of an amount per coin (measured as the average of a sample of not

Figure 30 – Title Page of Decimal Currency Act 1967.

CH. 19   151

Decimal Currency Act 1969

1969 CHAPTER 19

An Act to make further provision in connection with the introduction of a decimal currency, and to impose restrictions on the melting or breaking of metal coins. [16th May 1969]

B E IT ENACTED by the Queen's most Excellent Majesty, by and with the advice and consent of the Lords Spiritual and Temporal, and Commons, in this present Parliament assembled, and by the authority of the same, as follows:—

1.—(1) Coins made by the Mint in accordance with section 2 of the Decimal Currency Act 1967 or in accordance with the Coinage Acts 1870 to 1946 and not called in by proclamation under paragraph (5) of section 11 of the Coinage Act 1870 shall be legal tender as follows, that is to say— *Legal tender.*

1967 c. 47.

1870 c. 10.

> (a) coins of cupro-nickel or silver of denominations of more than ten new pence or two shillings, for payment of any amount not exceeding ten pounds ;
>
> (b) coins of cupro-nickel or silver of denominations of not more than ten new pence or two shillings, for payment of any amount not exceeding five pounds ;
>
> (c) coins of bronze, for payment of any amount not exceeding twenty new pence or four shillings.

(2) In the foregoing subsection "coins of bronze" includes threepences of mixed metal.

(3) Subject to subsection (6) of this section and to any direction given by virtue of section 15(5) of this Act, coins of the old currency other than gold coins shall not be legal tender after the end of the transitional period.

Figure 31 – Title Page of Decimal Currency Act 1969.

Figure 32 – The United Kingdom's first decimal coins (1971).

DECIMAL DAY
MONDAY 15th FEBRUARY 1971

- On this day—D Day—the United Kingdom will officially change to decimal currency.
- The pound sterling (£) will be divided into 100 new pennies (100p). There will be a new halfpenny (½p).
- The three bronze coins will not become legal tender until D Day. But the other coinage changes will be made gradually from 1968 onwards.
- The 5p and 10p coins have the same size, weight, and metal content as shillings and florins and are interchangeable with them; they will come into circulation from 1968.
- The sixth decimal coin will be the 50p. It will replace the 10s. note well before D Day. The halfpenny will cease to be legal tender on 1st August 1969, the half-crown on 1st January 1970, and the penny, threepenny bit and sixpence after the changeover period.
- The changeover period will last for several months after D Day; except on cheques, both currencies will be in use and £p will gradually replace £sd in shops and offices as cash registers, office machines, and slot machines are converted or replaced. Enquiries please to: The Decimal Currency Board, Standard House, 27 Northumberland Avenue, London WC2

see overleaf

BRITAIN'S FIRST DECIMAL COINS

Britain's new decimal coinage breaks away from a system of counting coins dating back to Anglo-Saxon times. There are three bronze coins (the ½, 1 and 2 new penny) and two cupro-nickel coins (the 5 and 10 new penny).

The obverse (by Mr. Arnold Machin, Q.B.E., R.A.) shows the Queen wearing a diamond tiara, a wedding present from Queen Mary. This portrait is also used by Australia, Canada and New Zealand.

The reverse designs are by Mr. Christopher Ironside. Their heraldic descriptions are:

½p The Royal Crown.
1p A Portcullis with chains royally crowned, originally a badge of King Henry VII, but for long closely associated with the Palace of Westminster.
2p The badge of the Prince of Wales. Three ostrich feathers enfiling a coronet of crosses pattée and fleurs de lys, with the motto "Ich Dien."
5p The badge of Scotland. A thistle royally crowned.
10p Part of the crest of England. A lion passant guardant royally crowned.

see overleaf

Figure 33 – Contemporary information for Decimal Day 1971.

Discussions about metrication

The British Standards Institution had put out a short statement in May 1962 to stimulate discussion on the subject of metrication. In the October of 1963 a more important statement was made by the BSI, based on the views of its own committees which formulated the main standard specifications used in industry and commerce. This statement indicated that there was a substantial majority view that changes were inevitable in the field of measurements. These changes, the BSI reported, should be directed towards the introduction of the metric system as the primary system of weights and measures in the UK within the shortest possible period of time. Great stress was laid on the need for a decision on this matter as soon as practicable, since indecision was acting as a direct curb to industrial progress.

The CBI spent nearly the whole of the year 1964 consulting trade associations about the possibility of a change to the metric system in the UK. Two main types of objection emerged from these enquiries. The first, pressed most strongly by the brewing industry, related to the difficulty anticipated in getting the change across to the general public; the second related to the difficulties that some firms, particularly in engineering, would have in relation to their business in the USA. The general consensus of opinion, however, was in favour of a change to the metric system. There were thirteen trade associations definitely in favour of the proposed change, and these included some of the large and powerful associations. There were eight other associations who agreed that the change was inevitable but not urgent There were two associations that did not want the change but were willing to fall in with the majority opinion. Lastly; two associations were definitely opposed to any change, and two others wished to retain both imperial and metric measures.

As a result of the above enquiry and after further internal consultations the President of the CBI sent on 17 February 1965 a letter to the First Secretary of State, the President of the Board of Trade and the Minister of Technology. The following is an outline of the contents of this important document which really initiated the change of attitude leading to adoption of the present policy on metrication. A significant change in outlook amongst industrialists had taken place in the preceding two years. A majority, both in numbers and in total size, of British industry now favoured the adoption of the metric system as the primary system of mensuration for British industry 'as soon as that can brought about by general agreement'. This last phrase was intended to indicate the voluntary nature of the proposed change, but it was realised that the determining factor in achieving this objective would be the attitude of the Government to these proposals. The letter ended by suggesting that the time was ripe for a general statement of policy by the Government expressing support for the general principle of change. It also suggested that Government Departments, in placing contracts, could do much to promote metrication in appropriate sections of industry; provided that there was consultation with the suppliers concerned.

As a result of this letter a meeting was held on 28 April 1965 between representatives of the CBI, the Board of Trade, the BSI, the Department of Economic Affairs, and the Department of Scientific and Industrial Research. Some of the suggestions made at this meeting formed the basis of certain parts of subsequent Government action.

On 24 May 1965 the President of the Board of Trade, Mr Douglas Jay, made an agreed statement in the House of Commons on behalf of the Labour Government supporting the proposals of the CBI for a phased change to the metric system in the UK.[161] Amongst the points made in his speech were:

(a) The Government considered it desirable that British industry, on a broadening front, should adopt metric units, sector by sector, until that system could become in time the primary system of weights and measures for the country as a whole.

(b) The Government hoped that within 10 years the greater part of the country's industry would have effected the change.

(c) The Government would make additional funds available to the British Standards Institution to enable it to accelerate the process of providing the necessary metric working standard specifications.

(d) Encouragement to change to the metric system would be given where practical by seeking to arrange that tenders for procurement by the

Government and by other public authorities should be in terms of metric specifications.

In March 1966 the Government set up the Standing Joint Committee on Metrication with the following terms of reference: 'To encourage, assist and review the progressive adoption with British industry of the metric system of weights and measures'.[162] This Committee consulted all Government Departments and a very wide range of industrial interests, as well as the Royal Society and the Council of Engineering Institutions.

In view of the subsequent controversy in Parliament relating to the activities of the Labour Government during the period 1965–1970, it is interesting to note that on 27 October 1966 the President of the Board of Trade was asked in the House of Commons 'whether he will adopt the metric system for all units of measurement in the United Kingdom'. The reply was 'No, Sir. The Government's view is that the first step is to encourage industry to adopt the metric system'.

The Report of the Standing Joint Committee on Metrication was submitted to the Minister of Technology by the Chairman Mr A H A Wynn on 14 May 1968. The Minister, Mr A Wedgwood Benn, announced in the House of Commons on 26 July 1968 the Government's acceptance of the report. He stated that the Report made three main recommendations. 'First, that manufacturing industry can make the change efficiently and economically only if the economy as a whole moves in the same direction on a broadly similar time-scale and in an orderly way. Second, that a Metrication Board should be established to guide, stimulate and co-ordinate the planning. Thirdly, that any legal barriers to the use of the metric system for all purposes within the United Kingdom should be removed.' Although the recommendations were being accepted, Mr Benn made clear that 'No compulsory powers will be sought. There can be no question of compensation; the costs of adopting metric weights and measures must lie where they fall'. The Government, he said, accepted 1975 as the target date for all provisional programmes. It also accepted that the legislation needed to remove obstacles to the adoption of metric units would be provided.

This statement was clearly a very important one, particularly in accepting that manufacturing industry was not to be alone in moving towards full metrication. Surprisingly enough, Mr Benn's statement in the House of Commons was met part way through by cries of 'Too long', and he was required to justify his continuation to the end of this policy statement. In reply to a question, Mr Benn made clear that the cost of metrication could not be stated; other countries that had already gone metric had been unable to do this. Again, in reply to further questions, he assured the members present that compulsion was not a part of the process.

The Metrication Board was set up in 1969 to facilitate the transition from the use of the imperial system of weights and measures in the UK to the metric system. The Board was not given any mandatory powers; its functions were purely advisory, educational and persuasive. The process of metrication in the UK was, in fact, well under way when the Board was set up; this seems to have escaped the notice of some opponents of metrication who painted the Metrication Board in subsequent years as an evil genius usurping the function of the Members of Parliament!

An interesting point in social history arises here. The law passed in 1897 making the use of metric units permissible in the UK did not bring about metrication because there was no element of compulsion in the wording of the Act. In 1965 there was again no mandatory legislation, but the effect is the same as if there were compulsion to carry out Government policy. The main reasons why a Government decision in this matter does not need to be enforced by legislation are summarised in the next section.

Further moves towards full metrication

The greatest lever in the hands of the Government to produce the desired change is the tremendous volume of what can be roughly classified as Government spending. In 1968 this amounted to £11 000 000 000 (11 gigapounds). It is not only Government Departments as such, but also the Nationalised Industries, the Post Office, and the various Defence Establishments which can require their suppliers to tender for contracts in metric terms or for goods with metric dimensions. In the construction industry in the UK more than half of the total volume of work was either on Government account or for bodies such as Local Authorities who receive substantial financial support from national funds. Electrical manufacturers reported that in 1969 about one third of the industry's whole output of over £3 000 000 000 (3 gigapounds) was dependent upon public purchasing policy; in certain sectors of the electrical industry as much as 70% of the output was, directly or indirectly, on Government account.

There were other forces which could be brought into play for a Government fostering the process of metrication. Prominent amongst these are the policies of the Department of Education and Science, the Industrial Training Boards, and the British Standards Institution; this last body only receives part of its income from Government sources. There is little doubt, therefore, that in the future, complete metrication of the industry and commerce of the UK will eventually be an accomplished fact. Although ostensibly the change to the metric system in the UK had the backing of industry, and hence might be said to be a generally accepted voluntary process, it is clear that Government policy was the deciding factor in starting the process of change to the metric system.

Although legislation of a compulsory nature was not required to initiate metrication, there had to be passed a series of enactments coming under the general description of 'enabling-legislation'. Several Acts of Parliament that were on the Statute Book, relating to specific industries or branches of commerce, laid down a limited number of values of weights and measures for certain particular transactions and these were quoted in imperial units. Thus pre-packed quantities of butter, sugar, tea, flour and several other items could at first be sold in the UK only in the standard amounts laid down by Parliament. Since metrication had not been envisaged when these particular regulations were made, the quantities specified for both the retail trade and in some sections of general commerce were in imperial units, and it was illegal to offer for sale packages or other quantities of the specified commodities in terms of other units. Enabling legislation was introduced in 1994 to make packages of the restricted commodities to be labelled (from 1 October 1995) in metric sizes corresponding to these imperial sizes, these latter values of which were permitted to be printed in somewhat less conspicuous type.

On the Continent the practice of restricting sales of particular goods to fixed values is not encountered so far. Ever since the election of a Conservative Government in 1970 the introduction of the many separate items of enabling legislation has been hindered by the opponents of metrication with the result that full metrication had not been achieved even at the beginning of 1996, that is 20 years after the target date.

From the financial point of view there was no Government subsidy available for firms involved in extra expenditure arising from the process of metrication. There was, however, for taxation purposes permissible premature write-off of capital equipment when imperial items were replaced by metric items. It was clear that some firms would be hit harder than others, but in the official phraseology 'the costs must lie where they fall'. The nation as a whole is paying a heavy penalty for the lack of foresight by certain people of past and present generations.

The following are the main two persuasive reasons for the adoption of the metric system of weights and measures in the UK. Firstly, the use of the metric system is almost world-wide, and amongst the main trading nations of the world only the United States has remained a user of the imperial system. In terms of population approximately 95% use metric, and 5% the various non-metric systems. Roughly 90% of world trade is conducted in metric weights and measures.

Secondly, more than 90% of Britain's exports go to metric countries. It has thus been possible to eliminate to a large extent the position of having one production line for exports and another for the home market. Some people have read into this situation the theory that the decision by the UK to metricate was influenced by application to join the European Common Market; this is not the case, since the pressure for metrication pre-dates the EEC by many a decade.

Progress: 1965 to 1970

During the five years from 1965, metrication had been completed in 15 minor but important sectors of industry and commerce, and the remaining sectors were well advanced in their planning and partial execution. Early in 1970 the CBI had reported to its members that the Ministry of Technology (in the Labour Government) was moving towards the drafting of the 'Enabling Bill' that had been long awaited. This Bill would be necessary to deal with certain issues and amendments to legislation which could not be covered by delegated powers such as the one relating to pharmacy. The CBI reported that joint consultations with the Government on this matter were being arranged.

In June 1970 the election of a Conservative Government resulted in a definite setback to what had been a relatively smooth progression towards a clearly-defined goal.

There was due about this time the need for a Statutory Instrument which would enable sand and ballast, together with ready-mixed mortar and concrete to be sold in metric quantities, whilst still allowing sales to continue where desired in imperial units. This amendment of Schedules 5 and 7 of the *Weights and Measures Act 1963*, to become operative on 1 January 1971, had passed through both Houses by 21 July 1970. In the Commons the then Minister of Technology, Mr Geoffrey Rippon, had said that 'where individual industries had voluntarily progressed to the point where amendments to regulations couched in non-metric terms become necessary, the Government are prepared after consultation with interested parties to introduce amendments under existing statutory powers' . . . 'On the other hand', he continued, 'the Government are not yet committed to general enabling legislation involving amendments of Statutes. Before such legislation is introduced it is intended to provide time for the matter to be debated in both Houses of Parliament after the recess'. The promise of a debate on the subject before further enabling legislation would be considered, came, according to newspaper reports, as a concession to Conservative backbenchers who were preparing the ground for an anti-metric drive in the House. The number of MPs concerned was reported variously as 72 and 75, which represents a relatively strong group in a Government with a majority in Parliament of the order of 30 members.

1970: The Parliamentary Debate on Metrication

The promised debate was held in the Commons on 27 October 1970 and in the Lords on 30 November 1970 (postponed from 11 November). In the Commons the debate was opened by the Minster for Industry, Sir John Eden; there were very few Labour Members present and the Conservatives who were present seemed to be mainly those who were hostile to the whole process of metrication.

Sir John Eden made clear in his opening remarks that there was 'no question of going back on the position – to put into reverse what has already been done by industry'. He added, however, that the retail trade would not necessarily be compelled to conform. On the whole, his speech as printed in Hansard seemed to be an excellent statement of the situation that existed and the consequences that would flow therefrom. There must, however, be something in an orator's tone of voice or perhaps that general demeanour which cannot show in the printed word, and in this case the low key in which Sir John Eden had spoken seemed to have given some satisfaction to the anti-metric members present. He seemed to leave it to Mr Wedgwood Benn who had been the Labour Minister of Technology to answer the objections raised by the members of his own party. In particular Mr Benn said that the accusation that metrication had been introduced by stealth was quite false; everything had been done openly by way of public surveys, consultations and public debate. There had been no move when the Labour Government was in power for a debate on the subject by the Conservative opposition. Some of the speeches made by the anti-metric group of Conservatives were extraordinary, as is shown in the following paragraphs.

Mr Robert Redmond said he was glad 'to hear the Minister say that the brakes will be applied slowly'. He then added 'When I have travelled abroad and particularly on the Continent, I have noticed that people have on their desks calculating machines while we in Britain do the same sums in our heads. I suggest that this is because we have been taught the imperial system in our schools alongside the metric system'. At that time Britain was still in negotiation with the six countries of the EEC. Alluding to this, Mr Redmond continued, 'I believe that if the Chancellor of the Duchy of Lancaster comes back with the most wonderful conditions for our joining and has the greatest success in the negotiations, the British people must still be carried with him. In other words, they must not have metrication forced on them against their will. Indeed, too fast a move in the direction of metrication might even prevent us from getting into the EEC'!

Mr John Page praised Mr Redmond who had 'brought a breath of common sense and fresh air' into the debate. He then 'noted with relish the lack of enthusiasm' with which Sir John Eden had introduced the debate. Mr Page then denied that the world was going metric and quoted a friend of his who had bought half a kilogram of 2 inch nails in Holland! He then said that there had been 'some slipshod discussions by the S. I.'! The only prominent body with the initials S. I. is the Socialist International, but he could hardly have meant this. A clue to the origin of some of this planned opposition to metrication might possibly be found in his citation of the beer and milk producers' opposition to the change, and his contention that metrication will be to the benefit only of particular manufacturers. Mr Page made a specific plea for a halt to the whole process of metrication pending the report of a new commission he wanted to have set up to go into all the details; which, he said, had not been made available. The Metrication Board should either be disbanded or put into cold storage until his proposed commission had reported to Parliament, and a clear mandate obtained to go ahead with metrication. He said that the Ministry of the Environment and the Ministry of Defence should cease to call for tenders to metric specifications; the Ministry of Education (sic) should call a halt to the process in school, for, he said, 'it is extremely dangerous for our children not to be taught about pounds and feet, inches and yards'! Mr Page wound up by saying, 'During the last election one of the reasons why the Conservative Party was returned was because most of our candidates said that we were determined to consult the people, to listen to the wishes of the people, to keep in closer touch rather than become separated from them as the previous Government had become'.

Mr Roger White repeated the £5000 million value for the cost of metrication, but without identifying his source. He also stressed the need to consult the people! Curiously enough, he asked the Minister to tell us, 'Where has the centimetre gone?'.

Captain Henry Kerby made a really vitriolic speech, pouring scorn on the whole business, and bringing in again that accusation that the whole business of metrication had been proceeding by stealth: '. . . this metric madness, this alien academic nonsense, introduced secretly through the back door by a bunch of cranks and the big business tycoons . . .' and '. . . put into clandestine operation'. The reason for the change, he said, was to show that Britain was trendy and 'with it'. He asserted that the Americans had got to the moon without metrication, and in France the common sense of the ordinary people still rejects the metric system imposed on them by revolutionaries!

Miss Joan Hall was honest in acknowledging her small knowledge of the subject and seemed to think that the general mass of people was equally confused. One thing she asserted that she knew was that '1 degree centigrade is freezing point'!

Mr John H Osborn said that the general public did not know enough of what was going on. He also mentioned costs, and attributed the figure of £5000 million to the British Equipment Trades Association. He felt, however, that we could not turn back; the decision to foster metrication had been made but the method by which it was taken was open to criticism.

Mr Ronald Bell repeated that 'All this has been done by stealth'. After citing public building construction and Education as Government provinces where metrication was proceeding apace he said, 'And all this in a parliamentary democracy without the Legislature having been so much as asked. It does indeed raise constitutional questions . . . This is not just failing to take the public along with you: it is very close to showing a supercilious contempt for the whole democratic process and the place that Parliament occupies in our constitution'. He then went on to say that although the Government as purchasers had been performing an executive act and not a legislative one, the Executive had in fact used its enormous purchasing power with public funds to change the system of weights and measures in the Country without going to Parliament. He said people in the consituencies were under a false impression that there had been an Act of Parliament which had done this, 'yet the whole thing was a facade, a conspiracy and a deceit of the public and an evasion of Parliament'.

Mr Carol Mather said that during the election campaign he was asked a number of questions about metrication but he could not answer them. However, since then he had 'done his homework' with the result, he said, that 'I am led to the conclusion that comprehensive universal metrication is a bit of a nonsense'. He then criticised the SI system (sic) because 'there is a gap between the millimetre and the metre, there is no centimetre . . . The kilo is too heavy for the housewife to carry and we know that in France and Denmark they use the old system of the pound.'!

An unfortunate consequence of all this opposition to metrication by this group of Conservative MPs was the announcement by Mr Julian Amery on behalf of the Government at the end of the debate that a White Paper on the subject would be published before proceeding with further legislation. Had this come out within a few weeks, no great harm would have been done, but it was actually 16 months before the White Paper appeared. In the interim, uncertainty replaced the steady progress that had hitherto obtained.

The debate on metrication in the House of Lords on 30 November 1970 was a more balanced affair. The Earl of Halsbury said that the figure of £5000 million for the cost of metrication in the UK bore no relation whatsoever to known engineering costs. As an example of the present absurd situation he pointed out that a bottle of whisky contained $26\frac{2}{3}$ fluid ounces, resulting from 2 gallons being used to fill 12 bottles; actually this quantity works out in metric measure at 750 mL per bottle which is a much more convenient number. Lord Shepherd said, 'I do not know why the Government have got themselves into their present difficulties. Certainly the reaction of industry was bad after the debate' (in the Commons). This last point was an important observation.

Press comment and other dampeners

The reaction of some of the newspapers was quite unrealistic, particularly after the October debate. A leader in *The Daily Telegraph*

(2 November 1970) said that 'The backbenchers from both sides of the Commons in last week's debate [on metrication] blew, God bless them, a resounding raspberry – not only at the methods employed by the last Government but also at the nature of the proposition itself'. In an article in *The Times* of the same date Mr David Wood not only showed a complete misreading of the situation but seemed to be completely unaware of the harm that was being done to the Country by the group of Conservative backbenchers on whom he showered such praise. According to Mr Wood a new situation had arisen. The two Statutory Instruments providing for metrication in the sand and ballast trade and in pharmaceuticals 'will not be fought to a division tonight'. As a *quid pro quo* he said the Government had agreed to produce a White Paper and the Bill being urgently drafted in the Ministry of Trade and Industry on the original orders of Mr Wedgwood Benn would be pigeonholed. The target of 1975 for what he called 'statutory metrication' was therefore abandoned. He then gave what can only be described as a caricature of what had happened since 'near the beginning' (actually four years after the beginning) when Lord Richie Calder and the Metrication Board brought out their first report. This was, said Mr Wood, 'For any democrat or parliamentarian . . . a shocking document, or so Conservative MPs thought' . . . The revelations of 'bureaucratic arrogance', went on Mr Wood, 'were breathtaking'. The Ministry of Technology had been plotting to introduce *as soon as possible* a general metrication Bill, which, amongst other things, would provide for 'the authorisation and definition of units of measurement which are to be used *for all purposes in this country*'.

It seems that not only MPs but also journalists can sleep whilst things are happening all around them quite openly and without their taking notice. 'Under Labour Ministers', continued Mr Wood, 'one Whitehall Department after another was forcing its suppliers to go metric. Tenders had to be metric, or the Government would do no business. Whitehall knew best. Participation? The will of the people? Out of the topless tower of Mintech came a hollow laugh that reverberated to 22 Kingsway where the Metrication Board work by stealth'! But this nefarious business could not last; a General Election resulted in Mr Geoffrey Rippon taking office at the Ministry of Technology.

Reporting the debate in the Commons on 27 October Mr Wood stated, 'Leading for the Government, Sir John Eden sounded as neutral as he dared and looked suitably embarrassed'. The anti-metrication men saw their chance. They drafted a warning motion that took the Government by surprise, and within a few days Government business managers had entered into negotiation behind the scenes with mutually satisfactory consequences. Long live the imperial pint: shades of 1904. In conclusion Mr Wood said that he wished that he knew how to say in metric terms 'that backbenchers last week added a cubit to their stature'. He would have had equal difficulty in saying this in imperial measure!

According to Nigel Lawson in *The Sunday Times* (8 November 1970) 'a reconsideration of the entire metrication programme was on the cards'. Many members of the present [Conservative] Government were barely aware when it took office that in 1965 their predecessors had launched a programme of making Britain wholly metric within the next five years. Mr Lawson then pointed out that 'There has been no White Paper, no Act of Parliament, not even a full-scale debate – just an administrative *fiat*'. He then went on to criticise the 'quality of the argument' about the benefits of metrication; this criticism merely seemed to reveal his own ignorance of the subject, and his cheap jibes in relation to education, scientists and engineers were hardly worthy of a 'quality' newspaper.

On 30 November 1970 Mr David Wood as Political Editor of *The Times* reported that the Conservative backbenchers stood a good chance of succeeding in halting the programme which would have led to full metrication.

In the House of Commons Mr John Peyton announced on 9 December 1970 that the Government had decided that the alteration of speed limit road signs would not be carried out in 1973 as planned by the previous Government and that there was no alternative date for this in mind. Mr Warren (Conservative) welcomed this statement 'because we were beginning to run pell-mell towards metric mania, which the general public does not like and does not want'. Mr Page offered his congratulations and said that 'the ordinary people of the country are delighted to hear that their views are being listened to by the Government'.

The members of the Metrication Board had by that time started to worry about the consequences of this and other adverse developments. As a former President of the CBI, the Secretary of State for Trade and Industry could not help being a supporter of the metrication programme, but he was reported to be 'having a tough job in persuading his Cabinet colleagues' (Giles Smith, in *The Times* 11 December 1970).

Industrialists expressed their fears concerning the changed atmosphere in relation to metrication since the advent of the Conservative Government. Mr R T Raven of Birmid Qualcast, Chairman of the Special Metric Panel of the Aluminium Federation, was reported as saying (*The Times* 27 July 1971) 'No clear leadership is forthcoming from the Government on the general question of metrication . . . statements in the House of Commons tend to be anti-metric and it is this uncertainty which is the major factor in impeding change'.

Colonel H de J Keays, Director of the Engineering Equipment Users Association, stated that his association comprised the biggest corporations in the private and public sectors of industry. Its members were working enthusiastically to complete that change to metric practice and they looked to the Government for leadership. On another occasion he had said that the debates in Parliament had destroyed confidence in the National metrication programme and had given rise in some quarters to doubts about Britain ever going completely metric. The overall programme, he said, might be delayed by three to five years as a result of the muddled situation following the debates. Answering questions in the House of Commons in October 1971 Sir John Eden, Minister for Industry, admitted that there was a certain amount of confusion and said that he was pressing on to get publication of the promised White Paper as soon as possible. He seemed somewhat confused himself since he finished up by talking of possible discussion on the White Paper 'before there is any question of introducing a Bill requiring metrication'. No such Bill was required; what was awaited most urgently was enabling legislation.

A leading article entitled *Canutes of Metrication* appeared in the Business Section of *The Times* on 25 January 1972. This described the situation at that date quite clearly, and rebuked the 'Canutes' who were endeavouring to disrupt the final stages of transition to metric usage in education and in the retail trade. Looking back at some of the other material published in the same newspaper, some readers must have wondered whether the staff responsible for the other part of the paper ever read the business section.

About this time there was much confusion in both the educational world and in the publishing world concerning the progress of metrication in the UK. Most schools had been well prepared for teaching in metric units and some examining bodies had started to set examination papers in metric units. Many publishers in the educational field were at a loss to know whether to keep publishing scripts written in imperial units or whether to publish entirely in metric terms. In November 1971 questions were asked in Parliament seeking elucidation of the position in the field of education and publishing. The Secretary of State for Education and Science at that time was Mrs Margaret Thatcher [to become Prime Minister 1979–1990].

Mr Winterton (Conservative) asked Mrs Thatcher whether she would now issue a circular to Local Education Authorities recommending them to take no further steps towards the introduction of metrication, 'either equipment or curricula, until a decision on the subject had been taken in Parliament'. Further questions of a similar nature were asked by two other Conservative MPs. It was pointed out, however, by Mr Alan Williams that private industry was of its own volition converting to metrication, and it was the then present Secretary of State for Trade and Industry in his CBI role who took the initiative in asking the Government to adopt metrication.

In reply to the various questions on this subject, Mrs Thatcher emphasised amongst other things the need for the continued teaching of imperial units for some time to come. In this respect Mrs Thatcher was a true prophet, but it was the Conservative Party which was responsible for the prolonging of the process of a change, one that was known to be inevitable.

When in 1970 Mr John Peyton had announced the decision of the Government to postpone metrication of road signs, his audience could hardly have envisaged the position in 1996 when after 15 years of continuous Government by Conservative administrations, visitors from Canada and Australia were to be astonished to find road signs in the UK still in imperial units.

Chapter VII Part 3

Metrication in The United Kingdom – 1972 to 1996

The 1972 White Paper

The long-awaited White Paper, entitled *'Metrication' (Cmnd 4880)* was published in February 1972. Probably its most useful function was to inform MPs and others in need of instruction concerning:

– the reasons for introducing metrication in the UK;

– the depth to which the Country was already committed to metrication from which there is no possibility of turning back.

The following are some of the salient points made in the White Paper.

(a) 'If we keep to the imperial system we could soon become the only major trading country using it.' Metric countries were already taking more than 80% of our exports.

(b) Membership of the EEC necessitates the change.

(c) Use of the metric system in the UK has been legal since 1897, so 'there can be absolutely no question of 'metrication by stealth'; nor is there any lack of parliamentary authority for the ways it has been becoming more generally adopted'.

(d) 'The move to metrication has been taking place over many years, but the Government believe that the time has now come when they must act to ensure the orderly completion of the process. In doing so they will not hesitate to take whatever steps are necessary to protect the consumer during the period of changeover'.

All this seems very satisfactory, but alas, the shadow of that Tory revolt still lingered on in the pages of the White Paper.

After mentioning the directive ratified by the EEC to the effect that 1 January 1978 was the target date for exclusive use of the prescribed units throughout the Community, the White Paper then goes on to say that 'we shall naturally need a longer period in which to complete the changeover'. It then states that the arrangements negotiated by the UK with the Community 'will ensure that units used in our legislation are retained until 31 December 1979. Where there are special reasons they may be retained for even longer'! All this, let it be noted, is despite the original UK target of 1975 for complete metrication.

Next we were told that the 'present system for showing speed limits and other road signs is unlikely to be changed for a very long time to come'. A further statement made in the White Paper is that the Government 'have no wish to discourage the sale of draught beer by the pint, but equally if anyone wants to buy it by the litre or half-litre that too should be lawful. The Government have at present no plans for changing from imperial units for the sale of milk'.

The White Paper continued by stating the obvious fact that Government Departments 'are substantial purchasers of industrial products and could by their purchasing policies deliberately hasten or delay the introduction of products conforming to metric standards . . . the Government will wherever practicable purchase to British Standards conforming to international recommendations. But they do not intend to use public purchasing to force the pace of metrication'.

No answer was given in the White Paper to the question itself had asked, viz: 'Is partial metrication possible?' The views of the CBI in 1970 were quoted. 'It never made much sense to talk of industry going metric in isolation. All parts of the economy are interdependent . . .' Neither support nor the contrary were hinted at.

A timid approach to the long-awaited plans for the introduction of enabling legislation is ventured in the Paper and it is made clear that the use of imperial measures would still be permitted alongside metric measures, in the hope that in due course the imperial measures would fall into disuse. When the sale of spirits and draught beer by the litre or its sub-multiples eventually becomes legal, it is stated that it would probably be undesirable to allow both imperial and metric measures to be used in the same bar 'to avoid the risk of confusion to customers'! It seems extraordinary that some educated people could consider the persistence of two different systems of units in a modern country. Mr L Cohen, Secretary of the Council of Science and Technology Institutes which represented some 60 000 professional scientists and technologists, put the matter quite clearly when he said that 'the worst possible situation for the country would be to have some of our units in the metric system while retaining the imperial system for others'.

A useful service provided by the White Paper was to make clear that the 'several unofficial estimates of the global cost of metrication' were never supported by any statistical evidence. 'No well-founded estimate exists or could exist'. After pointing out that it is 'not possible to aggregate or to make worthwhile generalisations from a few costs for particular undertakings that are known', the White Paper says that 'the expenditure will not be heavy'. In support of this statement examples of known or closely-estimated costs are given for particular organisations (not named). Since these are taken from those sectors of industry where the costs are likely to be the highest, the figures quoted have real significance.

It has been stated that the chemical industry has estimated its own cost at £6 million spread over about seven years, amounting to only 0·25 of 1% of the industry's anticipated total capital investment programme on new plant and equipment over the same period. A particular group of firms (industry not specified) having an annual turnover of £450 million spread over a period of seven years or approximately 0·4 of 1% of its turnover. A large company with an annual turnover of more than £325 million expected the gross cost of a very comprehensive change to be about £1 million which would be only 0·3 of 1% of its turnover if spent in a single year. This company has found that it is already making annual savings of about the same order of magnitude, and moreover recurring annual gains are a likely prospect. Data from other sources were very much in line with the above, as distinct from the alleged colossal overall figure of £5000 million.

When discussing costs it would be more to the point if opponents of the change had regard to the fact that there is being incurred an unnecessary item of expenditure due to the delay in implementing the change. Various estimates have been made concerning the cost of the delay in implementing the process of metrication once it has been decided. In general these estimates usually lie between 5% and 8%

per annum (cf *Australian Report*).[163] This is quite a serious matter and makes all the more regrettable the hiatus between the 1970 position in the UK and the full resumption of continuous progress. That has been impeded by the uncertainty of full Government support and the failure to pass the necessary enabling legislation.

European Economic Community Rules

The Council of the European Communities adopted in 1971 a 'Directive' relating to the units of measurement for use by members of the EEC. Such a Directive is a form of Community Law and thereby obliges all member states to amend where necessary their domestic laws to accord with the Directive within a period of five years unless special extension time has been negotiated. This particular Directive takes SI units as the basis for most of the legal units to be adopted throughout the community.

The Directive gives a list of units of measurement of the British imperial system, together with a statement that their status was to have been decided before 31 August 1976. It is a pity that this statement is not a categorical prohibition of the use of such units after the date named. Unfortunately the negotiations conducted by the UK with the original six members of the EEC resulted in permission for the use of imperial units by the UK until 31 December 1979, with an ominous addendum that where there are special reasons, imperial units may be retained even longer. The other countries of the EEC were required to keep to the time-table for conversion to the approved units by 31 December 1977.

In a Directive dated December 1976, two important changes were made for future practice. The spelling 'gram' was used to replace the spelling 'gramme' and the practice of spaces was introduced between groups of three digits after the decimal point.

One EEC item, not in the original CGPM text, was the validation of the var (reactive power in an ac circuit).

The Directive gives a list of the units the use of which were to be made mandatory as from 21 April 1978; these correspond exactly to the CGPM rules which are given in Chapter V. This statement did not apply to the United Kingdom which had asked for an extension of the time during which imperial units could still be used.

In the EEC Directive of 20 December 1979, again there was permission for the UK and Ireland to continue using units outside SI but it was stated that before 31 December 1989, a date would be set for the final termination of these units.

The abbreviation for litre was given as l or L. It was made clear that the SI prefixes may be used in conjunction with the names 'grade' or 'gon', and the symbol 'gon' was acceptable.

In 1975 a committee had been set up by medical practitioners in London for the 'Protection of the millimetre of mercury' for the measurement of blood-pressure. Other bodies supported this viewpoint, the main one being the World Health Organisation (WHO). As a result of these representations an EEC Directive marked 85/1 was issued on 18 December 1984. This resolved that the 'millimetre of mercury be retained in addition to the kilopascal as a unit for the measurement of the pressure of blood and other body fluids'. The same Directive authorised the use of the derived unit, the barn, in the field of nuclear physics.

In October 1988 it was made known that the British Government was proposing to retain the mile and the pint, but would not oppose the continued metrication of those items of commerce which were not already metricated. A proposed Directive from the EEC was said by Mr Francis Maude, the Corporate Affairs Minister, to be broadly acceptable to the Government.

The following is an outline of the 'Proposal for a Council Directive' issued by the EEC on 15 December 1988.

Chapter I puts the Troy ounce, used in commerce for dealing in gold and other precious metals, in the same category as units for permanent use.

Chapter II These units will be authorised in UK and Ireland until a date fixed by these Member States. The three units in question are specified as the mile (and its sub-multiples for road traffic signs), the pint for beer, cider and milk and the acre which could be used for land registration for the time being.

Chapter III does not alter the units listed in Chapter III of the previous Directive. It states that these units will no longer be used beyond 31 December 1994.

Chapter IV lists the following units, allowable only in specialised domains, which must not be used beyond 31 December 1999. These are:

The fathom for marine navigation only.
The pint and fluid ounce for beverages in returnable containers.
The ounce and the pound (avoirdupois) for goods sold from bulk.
The therm ($105 \cdot 506 \times 10^6$ J) for gas supply [though from 1994 the practice is to designate energy equivalents supplied in kWh – see page 249 – Ed.]

The debate in the House of Commons on the proposed Directive took place on 11 April 1989. The salient points of this debate are as follows.

Mr Francis Maude, in introducing the debate, pointed out that it was in 1965 that metrication was decided upon 'purely for domestic reasons in response to urging by the CBI and others; it had nothing to do then with possible membership of the European Community'. The education system in this country moved to the metric system in 1974 and by 1989 about 10 million children have been taught only in the metric system.

Although this proposed Directive would allow the UK and Ireland to set a date for the termination of the use of the remaining imperial units, it was pointed out that if the European Community decided to impose a termination date, the UK and Ireland would not form a 'blocking minority'.

Dual marking (imperial and metric) on all goods would be permissible until the end of the 20th century. Mr Maude stressed that these proposals would affect the use of imperial units only for the purposes of trade and not to measurements which are only a matter of custom and practice; an example of this would be the measurement of the length of a cricket pitch. The cost of retaining two systems of units in manufacture was estimated by the Institute of Production Engineers to amount to 3 per cent of turnover.

Typical of the loose comments made by opponents of metrication was the statement by Mr Anthony Beaumont-Dark (Conservative) that 'half the world will still use imperial measures'.

Mr John Fraser pointed out that 'the fact that we change from one system of measurement to another does not mean that we need to change the size or the weight of things; it is simply to change the way in which we measure things'. At the end of the debate a vote took place on the resolution before the House which welcomed the proposed Directive. This was passed by 107 votes to 27.

It might seem surprising that the acceptance by the Government of the need to complete the process of metrication should be marred by its endeavour to retain the pint and the mile. The popularity of the Government at this time was at a very low ebb due to its policies on the National Health Service and the Community Charge (Poll Tax) [repealed in 1993] and hence its reluctance to incur further unpopularity.

In February 1989 Mr Peter Bottomley, Under-Secretary of State for Transport, said that Councils [Local Government Authorities] are being encouraged to introduce metric signs in an effort to reduce 'bridge bashing' by foreign drivers. Since Council surveyors and architects already work in metric units, this advice will be easy to follow. This also shows the absurdity of retaining the mile for road signs. It was officially estimated at that time that the cost of converting the existing road signs would be at least 30 megapounds and could be as high as 50 megapounds.

Full metrication in sight

The year 1990 saw the end of official opposition to full metrication; the implementation of the policy however would not be completed until 1991, and more particularly, 1 January 2000.

In the case of road signs the Labour Government had planned to make the change over to metric units in 1973. However, this was frustrated by the election of a Conservative Government in 1970. When Labour came to power again in 1974 their overall parliamentary majority was so small that the Government could not introduce the necessary legislation with prospect of success. Few people at that time would have thought that the year 1995 would open with no change in this situation despite the fact that land survey in metric units had become well established throughout the UK. [though some changes were to be implemented later in 1995 – see pages 318–321 – Ed.]

The election of a Conservative Administration in 1979 did nothing to improve the situation regarding metrication, despite the fact that the UK is committed by EEC Directives to full metrication. Thus the continual drain of resources in industry persisted and further weakens the British economy.

In the early days of the process of metrication emphasis was placed by its opponents on the alleged heavy cost of changing over to the metric system in the UK. As time went on the heavy cost of working with both imperial and metric units was lost sight of. In 1980 the CBI had drawn to the attention of the Government this permanent handicap. In the engineering industry alone it was estimated that £1100 million per year was wasted in this way.

Opposition to metrication had come mainly from a group of people who held nostalgic views; regarding imperial measures as 'a British heritage'. They were probably supported in their views by some of the results of opinion polls. Many polls were 'loaded' in some such way as the following. At a time when there was widespread opposition to Britain's entry into the Common Market, a question was often phrased as follows: 'Do you favour a change in our weights and measures to the Continental system?'. Actually there was no such thing as a Continental system: what was in question was an International System. The word Continental was probably calculated to evoke a negative reply.

Future generations will be amazed at the continued opposition from official sources to the change-over to the metric system. Those who have time to study the imperial system will be surprised that so complicated a system should have persisted so long in the presence of the much simpler and more rational system.

The 1989 EEC Units Directive and the 1994 British Statutory Instruments

In 1989 the EEC Legislature passed the *Units of Measurement Directive 89/617/EEC*. Consequent on this the British Parliament had one of two realistic alternatives: either to wait for the import of the Directive to be imposed (and with barely a thought as to National considerations), or to bring in its own legislation towards full(er) metrication. The latter less painful alternative was chosen, and in November 1994 the Westminster Parliament approved six Statutory Instruments, as follows:

The Weights and Measures (Metrication Amendments) Regulations 1994-SI 1994/1851

The Weights and Measures (Packaged Goods and Quantity Marking and Abbreviations of Units) (Amendment) Regulations 1994-SI 1994/1852

The Price Marking (Amendment) Order 1994-SI 1994/1853

The Weights and Measures Act 1985 (Metrication) (Amendment) Order 1994-SI 1994/2866

The Units of Measurement Regulations 1994-SI 1994/2867

The Weights and Measures (Metrication) (Miscellaneous Goods) (Amendment) Order 1994-SI 1994/2868

These Instruments essentially took effect from 1 October 1995. The main consequences are listed below: [though these should not be construed as a full and definitive interpretation of the legislation].

Mandatory with effect from 1 October 1995

(a) Metric labelling (eg in grams, millilitres): for all pre-packaged foods; though the imperial equivalent may also be given *in a less prominent way*. This stipulation means imperial quantities and units after or below the metric amount, and usually in a less prominent type-face.

(b) Metric quantities for all meats (including offal and bacon etc) and fish.

(c) Metric quantities (litres, millilitres) for all liquids, eg oils, paraffin (but see exceptions in (j) below – the pint).

(d) Metric units for dress and furnishing fabric, building supplies, timber, sand, cement etc (though ready-mix concrete may be sold by the cubic yard).

(e) In matters legal: the police officer giving evidence in court will be required to say, for example: 'The man appeared to be about 1 metre

80 centimetres tall and weighed about 75 kilograms.' [Has this legal nicety been thought through?]

Permitted units and practice, retained until 1 January 2000 only

(f) Pounds and ounces: may be retained and used for sale of certain loose goods from bulk, eg nails, fresh fruit and vegetables, sweets from 'bulk' jars.

(g) Miles, miles per hour: for road signs indicating distances and speed restrictions. These imperial specifications will become subordinate and optional supplementary indications only, until full metricated road signs are progressively phased in.

Units and practices to be retained without limit of time:

(h) In descriptions at point of sale: imperial quantities may be used (provided they are not false to a material degree). Thus the seller might describe items in terms such as 'a two-inch paint-brush', 'a three-foot bed', 'two-inch nails'.

(i) For some goods: eg jams, honey, peanut butter, cream, which were formerly sold in containers holding eg half-pounds, 12 ounces or pounds weight: such quantities are being retained, but the labelling is such that the exact equivalent metric weights are specified.

(j) The pint is retained – but only for draft beers etc, and also for milk in returnable glass bottles. (Such bottles are (from about 1993) marked 568mL).

(k) The acre – this reflects the fact that measurements and transactions in land are relatively infrequent occurrences.

Reactions against the October 1995 mandates

Within a few weeks of the Government's active promotion of the new metrication measures in September 1995, both old and new pressure groups were fighting to retain imperial units. It was pointed out that gunmakers in Germany produced rifles of bore diameter 0·22 inch and 0·303 inch. A chartered surveyor, Vivian Linacre founded the Imperial Measures Preservation Society. *The Times* (18 September 1995) reported him to have commented on the poetic justice of challenges to metrication being lodged by the European Foundation at the European Court of Justice in Luxembourg. This complaint questioned the legality of 'criminalising' the continued use of imperial measures. On 1 October, George Gardiner (Conservative, Reigate) called for a campaign of civil disobedience to preserve imperial measures and The Federation for Small Businesses suggested a 12-month transitional period, during which traders should be given the choice of selling goods in metric or imperial weights. (*The Times*, 2 October 1995).

Only time will tell the success or otherwise of this resistance.

A digression – the Renard series

Great cost benefits arise in production from the reduction of the numbers of classes of similar goods – though without reduction of the total numbers of items. This effect is known as economies of scale. In the planning of new lines, types, sizes and categories of goods to be manufactured to metric specifications, advantage can be taken of a more scientific approach than was possible in the early days of technological development. Much use is likely to be made of the Renard series of preferred numbers, the basic idea of which is described below.

When a range of sizes of a manufactured article is being planned, two considerations arise. The first is the ratio of the largest size to the smallest size, and the second is the increments between sizes. The first criterion is likely to be determined by external factors, such as the requirements of particular customers, or physical limits to the extremes of the proposed range of sizes. The second consideration is of the utmost importance and determines the future scope of the items in the commercial field and has strong bearings on the economics of the whole production process. It has been found by experience that in engineering, for example, best use can be made of a series of sizes which are in geometric progression, rather than in arithmetic progression. Consider for example the geometric series ½, 1, 2, 4, 8. Each number is twice that of the previous number; the percentage increase in size from 4 to 8 units is the same as the percentage increase in size from 1 to 2. In the case of an arithmetic series, however, this percentage increase from one size to the next differs widely throughout the set. If we consider the arithmetic series ½, 1, 1½, 2, 2½, 3, 3½, 4, 4½, 5, 5½, etc, the percentage increase from ½ to 1 is 100% but the percentage increase from 5 to 5½ is only 10%.

It was suggested by a French engineer Charles Renard that in a denary system such as the metric system; if, for example, the largest planned size is 10 times that of the smallest size, then the intermediate sizes should be determined by each one being a particular root of the number 10. If, for example, 4 intermediate sizes are required, then their geometric ratio should be $\sqrt[5]{10}$. If 9 intermediate sizes are required, then they should be in the ratio to each other of $\sqrt[10]{10}$. The beauty of this idea is that, suppose there had originally been practical scope commercially for the 4 intermediate sizes only, and that subsequent developments had made it necessary to increase this to 9, then the original 4 are a part of the expanded system of 9 intermediate sizes.

This description is only an outline of the subject; to bring out the point that the introduction of metrication has brought with it an opportunity of rationalising what were hitherto practices based on intuitive, rather than rational, decisions.

The use of such series as given in the examples is not confined to an overall ratio of 10 between the largest and smallest; the series can be extended upwards or downwards by multiplying or dividing repeatedly by 10.

A further digression – paper sizes

An interesting application of metrication is that of the standardisation of paper sizes; by the elimination of a bewildering array, to a rational and logical schema.

In the UK there were used up to the 1970s, 14 sizes of printing paper, 17 sizes of writing paper and drawing paper and 8 sizes of brown paper. Metrication has eliminated 18 sizes of paper in imperial measure. Strangely, photographic printing papers are available in sizes that still (1996) echo former imperial sizes, with curiously variable ratios of long side to short side.

Paper makers and printers in the UK decided on a rapid change to metric measures with a target date of early 1971 for completion of the change in most sections of the industry. Though books and news-papers do not commonly come within the scope of this rationalisation [though this is far more common in 1995 – Ed.], a most important development has been the policy of adopting for stationery and general printed matter the ISO series of 'A' sizes as the preferred format. This is a well-designed and systematic scheme for sizing paper and is based upon the following ideas.

The base size is of area one square metre and its sides are in the ratio:

long side : short side = $\sqrt{2}$: 1 = 1·414 : 1.

A little simple arithmetic then gives the values 1189 mm for the long side and 841 mm for the small side. The next smaller size is obtained by folding the paper over once, to give two sheets each with a long side of 841 mm and a short side of one half of 1189 mm which (in practical terms) is 594 mm; this gives the next smaller size one half the area of the original size and its sides are still in the ratio of $\sqrt{2}$ to 1. The base size is called A0, the next smaller A1, and the next A2 and so on down to the smallest size A10 which measures 26 mm × 37 mm. Table XXIII shows these 'A' sizes which are to be regarded as preferred sizes for normal use.

	Table XXIII			
	ISO range of A sizes of paper			
A0	841 mm × 1189 mm		A6	105 mm × 148 mm
A1	594 mm × 841 mm		A7	74 mm × 105 mm
A2	420 mm × 594 mm		A8	52 mm × 74 mm
A3	297 mm × 420 mm		A9	37 mm × 52 mm
A4	210 mm × 297 mm		A10	26 mm × 37 mm
A5	148 mm × 210 mm			

For general office work where foolscap size of paper has been in common use, the replacement size is the A4 sheet, which has now come into extensive use.

The A sizes have been accepted by most countries and in several of these the A sizes are mandatory. The amount of substance is specified in terms of its mass (weight) per unit area, using the gram and the square metre of paper surface. This book is to be printed on 100 gram paper. [1997 edition]

An advantage of the ISO range of paper sizes is now evident. If for example, an A0 sheet of a particular sort of paper weights 80 grams, then an A1 sheet of the same paper will weight 40 grams, an A2 sheet 20 grams, and so on. A ream of such A3 paper would weight 10 g × 500 sheets = 5000 g = 5 kg.

A current type of good all-purpose paper for office use is rated at 70 g/m^2. The complete range of stock paper sizes for ordinary use go from 20 g/m^2 up to 200 g/m^2. Wrapping papers are made in the range 17 g/m^2 up to 140 g/m^2. Thicker papers such as Manilla range from 135 g/m^2 up to 485 g/m^2.

Popular printing paper sizes available for photographers (1996) include the following:

Table XXIV		
Photographic printing paper sizes		
metric size mm	imperial size inches	long side : short side
89 × 127	3·5 × 5·0	1·43 : 1
127 × 178	5 × 7	1·40 : 1
165 × 216	6·5 × 8·5	1·31 : 1
203 × 254	8 × 10	1·25 : 1
305 × 406	12 × 16	1·33 : 1

Clearly, standardisation has yet to flush out this pocket of resistance.

Chapter VIII

The North American Scene

Introduction

This chapter outlines the past and present situation regarding metrication principally in the two 'developed' countries of North America. With so large a geographical area, and with such heterogenous populations, progress has been slow in the recognition of and adoption of systems of measurement so prevalent in other parts of the world.

Now that Mexico (with over 90 million inhabitants) is developing as an additional major industrial base, comprising a Common Market with the USA and Canada, the pace of progress in adopting metrication and SI is likely to accelerate. On 17 December 1992, four years after an initial Free Trade Agreement (FTA) between the USA and Canada, Mexico too became incorporated into NAFTA, the North American Free Trade Agreement. In spite of subsequent problems of these partners' economies, not least the increasing national debts and loss of market confidence particularly in Mexico in 1994 and early 1995, the existence of NAFTA is likely to speed the progress towards full metrication in this, among the largest of the collective free trade zones of the world, comprising some 360 million people.

The United States of America

In 1866 the metre was legalized in the USA but there was no encouragement to use it, and in 1884 Lord Kelvin appeared before a USA Senate Committee, advocating the adoption of the metric system. It was at the annual meeting in 1900 of the National Academy of Sciences (USA) that attention was called to the need for a common language of measurement and equipment measuring instruments conforming accurately to the standard; both lacking at that time in the USA. Instruments and other laboratory equipment had to be sent to Europe for accurate calibration and certification of accuracy.

A very important event in the USA was the creation in 1901 of the National Bureau of Standards (NBS). This eventually became the foremost laboratory in the world for measurements and standards. In 1902 Congressman Southard of Ohio introduced a Bill to make metric measure mandatory in all Government Departments, but the Bill failed to pass into law. In that very same year there were, for example, in Brooklyn alone still four different values of the (linear) foot, all legal.

A body was formed in New York in 1916 to promote the metric system in that Country. It was called the Metric Association. In the same year a pro-metric report was prepared by S W Stratton for use by American members of the International High Commission. Dr Stratton later left the NBS to become President of the Massachusetts Institute of Technology. Also in 1916 was formed the American Institute of Weights and Measures which proved to be strongly anti-metric in its policy. Provision was made in 1918 for the use of metric units by the US War Department. But the entrenched units comprising what has come to be known as the US Customary System remained, and still remains (in 1996), either dominant or co-dominant.

The National Bureau of Standards was constantly under suspicion of supporting the pro-metric lobby. This is understandable because most scientists throughout the world had worked in the c.g.s. system of metric units following its introduction in 1881.

Some consideration was given to metric units by the US Senate in 1921–1922, but nothing came of it. In 1923 *The Scientific American* in an editorial reported 'There exists no good reason at all why the metre-litre-gram system has not been adopted by the people of the United States'. Further submissions on the possible adoption of metric units were heard in the US Senate in 1926, but no action followed.

Steps were taken by the American Army in 1957 in connection with dimensions required to be metric. An important symposium of systems of units was held in Washington by the American Association for the Advancement of Science; this kept alive the interest in the search for improvements in the scientific use of units.

It was found necessary in 1958 to harmonise the various customary units of the USA, Australia, Canada, New Zealand, South Africa and the UK for the first time. The differences between units of the same kind in the several countries were very small; but by this time very high precision was required for practical purposes. The standard metre bar in Paris was an etalon of greater precision than any of the standard yard bars in the above-mentioned countries. Harmony and precision was then achieved by fixing the length of the yard as a definite fraction of the metre; the yard then became defined in all countries as 0·9144 metre precisely. This meant that the yard was still essentially a metric quantity.

The National Bureau of Standards adopted SI for use by its staff in 1964. In its report of 1967–68 it was stated that there had been some confusion in the missile and space rocket industry due to the mixed system of units. Probably the worst mistake was in mixing absolute and gravitational units. This led to the specification of rocket engine performance in improper units, as pointed out by A E Schuler in his article *Let's Quit Confusing Mass with Weight!*[178]

Specific impulse (I_{sp}) is the engine thrust in force units divided by the rate of propellant consumption in units of mass per interval of time, viz $I_{sp} = F/(M/T)$. Unfortunately it has been customary to give thrust in pounds force, and propellant consumption in pounds mass per second. The early workers erroneously cancelled the pounds in the numerator and denominator and ended up with I_{sp} in seconds! Actually the correct units are identical with velocity units. The error was so deeply entrenched in the rocket field that even modern workers who know better sometimes use 'seconds' to describe the performance of rocket engines. A newspaper article in 1971 stated that a nuclear rocket engine could have a specific impulse of 825 seconds 'as the specific impulse unit is generally abbreviated'. The above mistake would have been impossible with the use of SI units.

The system of units now being used by NASA is SI, and hence no confusion between mass and force will arise. Similarly, in such problems as those relating to the loading of structures situated on the moon where the value of g is only one-sixth of its value on earth, no problems will arise when using SI units.

In 1971 *The Machinery Handbook* (a USA publication) still gave the following information:

1 hand = 4 inches   1 span = 9 inches   1 quire = 24 sheets
1 ream = 20 quires = 480 sheets
1 ream of printing paper = 500 sheets
1 cord of wood = 4 ft × 4ft × 8ft = 128 cubic feet.

Starting in 1968, there was in the USA extensive investigation into metrication; costing some 750 megadollars, financed by Congress, and carried out under the auspices of the NBS. A 12-volume report entitled *A Metric America – a Decision whose Time has Come* was submitted to Congress in 1971. This included, amongst other things, the following points. The report recognised the inevitability of increasing use of the metric system in the USA. A planned national changeover from the present units was strongly recommended, envisaging something like 10 years to accomplish. The metric system should be taught in schools and the American public at large should also be made conversant with the system. There should be a firm Government commitment to a changeover to metric units, but each section of the economy should work out its own plans and timetable for the change. An important point was made by the authors of the report concerning the development of International Standards. It was indicated how very important it was for the USA to participate more actively in the framing of these Standards which, of course, were increasingly SI in their orientation. At that time the USA exported only about 4 per cent of its Gross National Product, as against about 14 per cent by the UK; nevertheless even this small percentage amounted to a considerable sum of money.

A pressure group called the American National Metric Council (ANMC) was formed in 1972 to promote metric conversion activities. The initial funding was provided by the American National Standards Institute (ANSI). At this time it was made clear by the NBS that this body was supporting strongly the use of SI in its external relations but that in the transitional period in the USA exceptions would be allowed in the interest of effective communication.

In connection with lubricating oils, agreement was reached in 1973 concerning the temperature at which the viscosity of an oil should be measured. The Anglo-American preference for 100°F (37·8°C) bowed out to the figure of 40°C, as recommended by the other members of the ISO Technical Committee.

In 1973 an American journal reported that a young lady – Miss Metric America – had a weight of 66 kilograms and a height of 18 centimetres! It is not known if this mistake was due to lack of familiarity with metric units, or was merely a typographical error.

The Metric Conversion Act of 1973 met with long and strenuous opposition in Congress: a brief outline of this Bill was reported to be as follows:

(a) to change the United States to the Metric System in a co-ordinated manner

(b) to implement this changeover through voluntary participation of all affected sectors

(c) to encourage the voluntary conversion of all sectors of the United States Economy to the predominant but not exclusive use of metric units within 10 years

(d) that changeover costs shall lie where they fall

(e) to assist in educating the public to think and work in metric terms.

It was surprising to find the American Trades Union movement producing vigorous opposition to metric conversion; whereas in the United Kingdom, Australia and Canada, the Labour movements were strongly in favour of the change to metrication.

In June 1974 the Metric Conversion Bill was defeated in the American House of Representatives, mainly due to procedural difficulties. However, the Full Senate passed Metric Bill HR 8674 in December 1975. This Bill did not set any deadline for a changeover. The Senate Bill provided for the establishment of a United States Metric Board; the Board had no enforcement powers. The Bill was signed by President Ford on 23 December 1975.

It was reported in 1977 that the American public's response to the metric system had been so overwhelmingly negative that the US Federal Highway authorities had abandoned a £60 million plan to convert distances on road signs from miles into kilometres. About 98 per cent of those questioned were opposed to the scheme; which was to have been completed by 1982. This was not surprising since, to put it bluntly, the public in America were largely ignorant concerning the metric system. Whereas in the UK school children have been taught at least the elements of the metric system in most schools since about 1900; the situation in the USA has been quite different. In the main, only students preparing to study science and technology in the USA have been schooled in the metric system. The US Metric Board which was included in the provisions of the 1975 Act was only formed in June 1978.

There were few indications that industry and commerce would fulfil the aspirations of the 1975 Act but these were mainly where international trade was concerned. A report by the Federal Reserve Bank of Chicago in 1976 said that in connection with the recent US move to adopt the metric system the bank predicted that this would 'lead to a reduction in costs and an elimination of dual-dimension products'. In the same year an advertisement in *The Times* (London) read as follows: 'The Tulsa (Oklahoma) Port of Catoosa offers the following facilities. Port channel 214 km long and 60 m wide, general dry cargo wharf 216 m long . . . 600 hectare Industrial Park'.

The weakness of the legislation of 1975 was in its permissive nature and lack of mandatory pressure. An example of what was happening occurred in 1976 when Mr Art Frier, Superintendent Schools Supervisor City of Los Angeles, stated that no more than 10 per cent to 12 per cent of the schools in the State of California would be teaching metric predominantly in the fall (autumn) of that year.

In aviation the main difficulty facing the advocates of metric units is the predominance of the USA in this field. The International Civil Aviation Organisation (ICAO) which has about 110 member nations has agreed to the introduction of metric units. However the main linear quantity is the nautical mile of 1852 metres and not the kilometre. Similarly the unit of speed is the knot (1852 m/h) and not the km/h. In manufacture the situation is even more difficult as far as the aerospace industry is concerned. The inch unified (coarse and fine) screw threads are used not only in USA but by the aircraft industries of other nations due to the overwhelming dominance of the Americans in this field. Actually many of these aerospace fasteners are expensive special types which would not normally be used for less exacting purposes in engineering generally. Nevertheless this means that non-metric screw threads will continue to be manufactured for many years to come. There was however pressure coming on USA manufacturers, due to their extensive capital investment in the European motor car industry.

In the USA itself the National Aeronautic and Space Administration (NASA) decided to adopt SI in 1970 and its official scientific and technical reports shall use this system of units. Moon reconnaissance charts are dimensioned in metric units. The Lunar Roving Vehicle ('Space Buggy') used by astronauts Scott and Irwin in 1971 during the Apollo 15 mission to travel on the moon's surface was equipped with computer control giving the distance traversed in kilometres. Its speedometer was calibrated in metric units, showing speeds from 0 to 20 km/h, both forwards and in reverse. Misunderstandings arose in newspapers due to the fact that for the purposes of popular broadcasting, values were given in customary units to suit the general public. There is no doubt that NASA now (1996) works in SI units.

It was once reported in the USA that a scientist gave the estimated exhaust velocity on a new type of rocket as 3×10^5 centimetres per second: his reluctant answer to the request by the Armed Forces for the value in English units was $1 \cdot 8 \times 10^7$ furlongs per fortnight.

The 1979 General Accounting Office Report, and after

The US General Accounting Office (GAO) is supposed to be a non-political arm of Congress which undertakes in-depth studies of issues of concern to Congress and the American People. A report by GAO on the economic and social impact metric conversion would have upon the American way of life was published early in 1979. A very wide range of organisations were consulted over a two-year period; which turned out to be a devastating indictment of the policy of the proponents of metrication viewed from the American angle. The following are some extracts from this report.

It is not the policy of the United States to change to the Metric system, the present policy has been misinterpreted.

No major benefits would occur to either producers, consumers or participants converting to the metric system.

Some reasons advanced in favor of conversion are now without foundation.

The 1975 Act and its legislative history show the national policy is not to prefer one system over the other but to provide for either to be predominant on the basis of the voluntary actions of those affected.

The Metric Board's responsibility under the 1975 Act is to devise and carry out a broad program of planning co-ordination, and public education, consistent with other national policy and interest, with the aim of implementing the policy set forth in the Act . . . The Board is not to advocate metrication but is to assist various sectors when, and if, they choose to convert.

There is no question but that one system should be predominant because the existence of a dual system for any length of time is impractical . . . It is not too late to make the decision as to which system is to be predominant.

Early in 1982 it was realised that the US Metric Board was on the point of extinction. Proponents of metrication failed to persuade Congress to continue to provide funds for this body. The Commerce Department was expected to help industrial and other organisations with metric problems, and subsequently inherit the remnants of the Metric Board and its files.

The Act of 1975 had made provision for Federal grants to be available in the educational field to introduce metric topics. By September of 1982 the metric education programme operated by Federal tax funds came to a halt: it was alleged that, amongst other things, the money had not always been spent wisely. At that time, US President Ronald Reagan disbanded the Metric Commission, stating that metric had 'walked its last kilometre' in America. However, in 1983 it was reported that the US Department of Commerce was back in business again promoting metrication. It assumed the duties of the defunct US Metric Board which was abolished by President Reagan. The Smithsonian Institution, one of the world's great scientific and cultural establishments, reaffirmed its commitment to metric usage in a memorandum published in 1984.

A digression: the American barrel

An American unit which has world-wide usage is the oil barrel; in metric terms this unit of capacity is equal to 158·987 litres. In the 'English' type of unit 1 barrel of oil USA measure equals 42 US gallons which is equal to 35 UK gallons. Approximately 7 barrels of crude oil weigh 1 tonne.

It is many years since oil was put into barrels and it would be a great advantage if the cost of oil and output of oil wells and of refineries were expressed in a more sensible unit. One possibility would be to use the hectolitre or alternatively the kilolitre. This assumes that volume will continue to be the criterion. If mass is chosen instead of volume, the metric tonne would have a clear advantage over the other different units with the same name of ton. Nevertheless the barrel of oil is likely to persist for many years, as the prices of oil continue to be quoted in US dollars per barrel (1996).

The absurdity of the name 'barrel' is seen in the diversity of size for the different relevant contents. In the UK the barrel of beer is equal to 288 pints. In the USA the practice in medieval England of separate barrels for beer and ale has persisted. The beer barrel contains 32 gallons which are the same size as the old English wine gallon of 231 cubic inches. The ale barrel contains 36 gallons each of 269 cubic inches. Another different barrel based on volume is that for alcohol, equal in value to 50 US gallons or 189 litres.

Two other barrels have their magnitude determined by weight instead of volume. One of these holds 280 lbs or 127 kg of salt. Another barrel holds 367 lbs or 166 kg of cement.

Not only is the American gallon in relation to petrol and other bulk liquids different from the UK gallon, but the small unit of capacity relating to domestic liquids called the fluid ounce is also different in the two countries. There are 16 fluid ounces in the American pint and 20 fluid ounces in the British pint, but to make things more complicated the USA pint is only 0·832 67 of the UK pint.

Antagonists and protagonists of metrication

Opponents of metrication appear to keep saying:

'Just why is the United States going metric after having lived with the English system for more than 200 years?' One answer to this might be that the American system of units is the English system of Queen Anne (1702–1714) and not the English system of the 20th century. This is why the Canadian system of units differed in many important ways from the American customary system.

Compared with the UK the USA had one advantage in that its currency was of decimal structure. The change in the UK from pounds, shillings and pence to a decimal currency upset some people and gave rise to fears that inflation would increase. On the other hand Britain had the advantage of a long tradition in teaching elementary metric concepts in the schools.

In 1965 when it was decided to adopt SI in the United Kingdom there was much discussion concerning the length of time that would be necessary to complete the changeover from imperial units. Some authorities thought that the proposed time of ten years was too long; others thought that the time necessary to complete the changeover would be much more than ten years. There was however a widespread opinion that in the United States of America a decision to adopt SI would be followed by a relatively short transitional period since the Americans can be great movers; they 'step on the gas' and get to their destination in a very short time. What was not realised by many people in the UK was that there are 'backwoodsmen' in the USA as well as in the UK; in fact such Americans seem to be more influential than their counterparts in the UK. The units of the US Customary System are certainly still part of the fabric of that Country, in 1997.

Some of the propaganda in the United States was not only absurd but in many cases was factually incorrect. Some examples are as follows:

'When England tried to convert in order to join the European Economic Community (EEC) . . .' The first mistake was to use the word England when it should have stated the United Kingdom. The second mistake (that of the suggested reason for conversion) has been repeated so often that many people have come to believe it. The decision in the UK to go metric was taken two years before Britain applied to join the EEC and eight years before Britain actually joined the EEC.

It was also said in 1983 that '. . . conversion was halted in England several years ago'. This is not true. A report in 1984 stated that 'The British had to back down . . . from metrication': again a false statement. It was further said in 1984 that 'The British Public waited until the Government tried to force metric on the consumer. An uproar was heard from coast to coast. That brought the end of the Metrication Board in a short time'. What a pity that the people in Britain did not hear this uproar!

Actually the Conservative Government in 1980 decided in the interests of economy to abolish a large number of QUANGOs (an acronym that stands for Quasi Non-Government Organisations). Such bodies are set up to advise the Government on some specific aspect of public life; some members would be paid by the Government but other would be giving their services voluntarily. The Metrication Board was regarded by the Government as a QUANGO ripe for abolition. To a certain extent this was true because the work of the Board was complete and the process of metrication was sufficiently advanced to preclude any possibility of reversal.

The narrow viewpoint of such American opponents on metrication is further shown by the two following quotations (uttered in 1984):

'It is estimated that 95 per cent of all nations around the world use some inch/pound units.' The evidence for this is not given. Also reported was the assertion, 'Exclusive metric is about impossible to find'. The author had clearly not looked very far.

In the process of metrication in the UK there have been two or three minor interruptions due to Parliamentary Procedure being used by a few ultra-traditionalists to prevent new regulations from being implemented. This again has led people in other countries to interpret a minor hiccup as an abandonment of the metrication process.

The strongest argument put forward by the opponents of metrication is that relating to the cost of conversion from customary to metric usage. These are short-term costs, and there is always saving in the long run. But even in the short run there are many cases where the saving is immediate. The following comment in an American Journal illustrates the point. 'Only big business benefits from the use of SI'. This bald statement is backed up by figures which do indeed show that American firms have saved millions of dollars by adopting SI. Then comes the fatuous assertion 'The public gets to pay the bill'! The truth is that economies in manufacture eventually lower prices to the public.

Some of the arguments against metrication show ignorance of the subject. One critic pointed out that many people are still using MKS units, and not SI. But, of course, SI is the MKS system expanded to allow it to embrace every branch of science and technology.

It is surprising that in these days of space travel that the USA should cling to an earth-bound system of units; the corresponding earth-bound system once prevalent in Germany using metric units has now been superseded by SI. These 'gravitational' systems of units were developed long before artificial satellites were envisaged.

Those Americans who cling to the yard and scorn the metre do not seem to realise that there is no standard yard; as previously indicated by definition the yard is a fixed fraction of the metre, namely 0·9144 metre exactly. From this it follows that the customary units of length, area and volume are fundamentally metric quantities, but with absurd relationships to the defining standards. In a similar manner, the pound mass is by definition equal to 0·453 592 37 kilogram exactly, thus acknowledging the primacy of the metric standard as the base unit of mass.

Controversy, ignorance, but eventual progress

There has been some controversy in the USA concerning the spelling of the word denoting the unit of length in SI. This word is spelt 'metre' outside the USA but is spelt 'meter' in that country. The case for the international type of spelling, viz 'metre' is based on the fact that in the English language 'meter' has another meaning, namely that of an instrument or similar device made for the purpose of making a measurement of some kind.

The case made by certain Americans against a change in their spelling is based on the fact that 'metre' is already a word in the English language relating to the composition of poems. But whereas practically everyone in the USA is familiar with the electricity meter or a gas meter or some such common item, relatively few of them are likely to be familiar with such terms as poetic trochee, spondee, dactyl etc. Likewise the 'metre' of poetry is an unknown quantity to most of them. We can enjoy poetry, even though few of us have met the word 'metre' in this connection.

There is no doubt that in all countries where English is widely spoken, the use of the spelling 'metre' would be of widespread benefit and of help in avoiding misunderstanding. It is also the spelling in most European and many other languages, and hence would be almost universal.

The educational aspect of systems of units has been largely forgotten by the opponents of metrication. In the UK the estimates made concerning the time saved by the teaching of SI to a pupil compared with the teaching of the imperial system ranged from about six months to a whole year.

The difficulty in teaching the imperial or customary system of units is well illustrated by the relative ignorance of the people who use it. In 1987 Professor Anton des Brasunas, University of Missouri, distributed a test paper amongst students and others to ascertain how much they knew of the customary system. He set 17 questions; and the results were that the average score was 4 correct answers. The position in the UK was very similar; hardly anybody knowing how many drams in an ounce. The lesson here is that the imperial and customary systems are difficult to learn and retain.

The fact that Congress voted in favour of permissive legislation in the matter of metrication seems to indicate that this would lead to a beneficial effect on the USA in the long run. The general public, however, seems to have rejected this notion. A question therefore arises as to whether or not Congress should proceed with further legislation in the direction of enforcement of a policy which scientists and technologists would like to see in the furtherance of a rational and advantageous system of weights and measures; to bring the USA into line with the rest of the world.

This type of situation has arisen from time to time in various democratic countries. Should the legislature impose on a democratic people a policy which is to their undoubted advantage, but which the people oppose at a particular time? This depends upon the agreed status of the legislators: are they delegates or representatives? If the former, they are mandated by their electors to vote in favour of the wishes of the electorate. If, however, they are acknowledged to be representatives, then they are free to vote for a policy which they think is to the advantage of the electorate, even if this is only in the long run.

One example of this paradox occurred in the United Kingdom before the advent of compulsory smallpox vaccination of children. After several epidemics of smallpox in the United Kingdom, attempts were made by legislation to introduce compulsory vaccination. A great crusade against compulsory vaccination resulted in the initial legislation for compulsion being too weak. The 1853 Act was followed by violent opposition; this Act 'violates the spirit of freedom and flies in the face of God': such was the popular cry. When further legislation increased the penalties for evading the compulsory vaccination of children the Anti-Vaccination League increased its efforts to overturn the legislation. There was also widespread opposition to compulsory vaccination in the United States, Canada and Australia. The great success of compulsory vaccination in eliminating the disease of small-pox has fully justified the action of the legislators in overruling public opposition to compulsory vaccination.

This is only one example of several cases where the cry of 'this violation of individual freedom' in a democracy has resulted in sub-sequent benefit to the people. These considerations should give weight to debate in the United States so that the possible long term benefits of metrication should not be lost.

It is of course a very serious matter for the legislators in any democratic country to pass a law which is known to be opposed by the majority of people in that country. It was Edmund Burke (1729–1797), an MP in the British Parliament, who first introduced the idea of a Representative as distinct from a Delegate in connection with the powers of a Member of Parliament. At that time his claim that Members of Parliament should act as Representatives was well founded. They were in general well educated whereas most of the electors were illiterate or nearly so. This situation only began to change in 1870 when Forster's Act brought elementary education within the grasp of all.

Since in the United States the general population at the present time is well-educated it might seem illogical for Congress to overrule their wishes, even though members of the Lower House are called Representatives. As against this must be set the fact that in the USA many of the general public are ill-informed concerning the metric system and know little or nothing about the subject of weights and measures in other countries.

An interesting effect of the oil crisis of the mid-1970s was that speed limits were reduced in order to save gasoline. The hitherto dual (metric/American Standard: ie kilometers per hour/miles per hour) speed restriction signs were replaced with eg 50 mph signs. As the oil crisis abated, these temporary restriction signs were then replaced with those bearing raised limits defined only in miles per hour.

One of the small steps towards the use of SI was taken in 1988 when President Reagan required the Federal Agencies to go to full metrication.

In 1992 the USA ceased to be the largest economic unit in the world, as in the year the EEC formed a single market. The USA cannot for all time ignore the fact that the EEC is committed to the use of SI by all its members.

Practice in 1995 where concession is made to metric units includes the practice of reporting illicit drug seizures in kilograms. Pharmaceutical products are usually prescribed and packaged in metric quantities.

Broadcast weather reports and forecasts in 1995 refer to temperatures in degrees Fahrenheit. Bulk timber is sold at say $400 per thousand board feet. The American board foot is a measure of volume being 12 inches × 12 inches × 1 inch. Nails – often referred to collectively as 'penny nails' – are sized as in Table XXV. In truth these units are relics that admit no indulgence.

| Table XXV |
| American 'penny nails' |

size of nail	approx length mm	approx length inches
4d	37	1½
5d	44	1¾
6d	50	2
8d	60	2½
10d	75	3
12d	81	3¼
16d	87	3½
20d	100	4
30d	113	4½
40d	125	5
50d	140	5½
60d	150	6

Canada

Almost from the date in 1965 when the United Kingdom decided to go metric, the Canadian Federal Government started to study the whole problem of metrication. The findings of their Metric Committee resulted in a Statement of Governmental Policy in the form of a White Paper laid before the Ottawa Parliament in January 1970. It seemed the time had come for positive metrication steps to be taken in Canada.

A Commission was set up 1971 representing a wide range of interest throughout Canada by means of many sub-committees. The Commission saw its task as falling into three broad areas – public information, education and implementation.

Since education in Canada is under Provincial jurisdiction [eg, Ontario, Quebec], the Commission had no legislative power. It had to depend solely on co-operation from the Provinces, which did in fact take place in the matter of education. The Commission did not aim at an all-dominant cut-off date which would make customary units unlawful; the plan was to metricate the various sections of the economy at a rate determined by the needs and co-operation of each sector. Beginning in 1972–1973, SI started to be implemented in stages within different areas within the Country.

On a nation-wide scale, a start was made in 1973 in the field of certain toiletries. The Federal Department of Consumer Affairs announced an immediate reduction in the number of package sizes of shampoos, skin creams, and lotions to be sold in Canada, the reduction to take place within two years. Such items would be packaged and marked in metric units only, with the volume expressed in millilitres. It should be noted that the regulation of weights and measures in Canada is under the control of the Federal Government, and not under the Provincial Authorities.

From 1975, weather forecasts were broadcast in metric terms: temperatures in degrees Celsius, rainfall in millimetres, and snowfall in metres. When the Metric Commission completed its mandate in 1985, metrication came under the Federal Ministry of Consumer and Corporate Affairs. Although there were pressure groups in Canada opposing metrication, a severe setback arose when the Conservative Government made good an election promise to not force Canadians to buy their gasoline (petrol) in litres and their pork chop in grams.

The really big obstacle to full metrication in Canada arises from its extensive trading relationship with the USA. In addition, television and other cultural interests from across the border have made continued progress in metrication in Canada very difficult. It is also surprising to read complaints from motorists crossing the border between the two countries that it is confusing to change from litres to gallons or *vice versa* when buying their fuel. One would have thought that it was even more confusing when crossing the border to change from gallons imperial to gallons USA when there was substantial difference in the two quantities each side of the border.

The setback to the process of metrication that had occurred when in 1984 the Tories removed the threat of prosecution for those who would sell imperial gallons of gasoline or carry on business in other measures of the past seems to have been modified subsequently. The Federal Conservative Government had by 1988 started to talk of seeing through the process of metrication; it was walking softly, encouraging rather than threatening. This policy would replace the blunt weapon approach of the former Liberal administration (Special Report in *The London Free Press*, Ontario, 23 May 1988).

By that time the commercial position in Canada had become very confused. The Consumers Association of Canada had been complaining of this for some time. The situation was in a mess, they reported; because of the return to imperial measures by some businesses that had made the switch to metric.

To outsiders it would appear that the completion of the process of metrication has a better chance of early accomplishment in Canada than in the USA because of the better foundations laid by the Provincial Authorities in their educational systems. By 1996 metrication was mandatory and hence virtually complete in Canada, though concessions to conservatives are found in the dual (imperial/metric) marking at many retail meat and fish markets.

Mexico, and hope for the future

As previously indicated, continuing momentum towards uniformity in measurement practice occurred from 1992 when the USA formed a common market with Mexico and Canada. These two latter countries are likely, in time, to influence the USA towards full metrication and the use of the International System of Units. Further, the consequences of over 5000 kilometres of undefended border between the USA and Canada are that relationships are strong. And companies with USA or Canadian manufacturing facilities (eg Degussa) are setting up factories in Mexico in order to exploit a pool of Mexican labour, where metric practice holds sway. Mexico, for its part, has large international companies that boast association with partners in the USA and Canada. Examples include Grupo ICA (Mexico's largest construction company); Grupo Tribasa, which has joint ventures with Bombardier of Canada; and Alfa, a large conglomerate, which manufactures carpets in association with Shaw Industries of the USA (*The Times (Mexico Supplement)* 15 March 1996).

Chapter IX

Final Observations

Introduction

These final remarks are intended to clarify certain matters and answer some questions that may have occurred to the reader.

Topics considered here include common errors, the decimal marker, motor vehicle fuel consumption, surviving non-metric units, large numbers, inconsistencies and problems of pronunciation. Naturally these matters cannot be exhaustive: the discussion here merely highlights a few areas of continuing confusion, debate and concern that are likely to be with us for the forseeable future. Some matters that did not fit conveniently into the main text are included in the Appendices. And, regretfully, no book can include selections that will satisfy all its readers.

Common errors

Although in recent years the BBC has taken an important role in the formulation of public opinion, the Press has still a powerful part to play in Britain in this direction. There are two ways in which the educational value of the Press can be of great benefit in the field of measurement. The first of these lies in avoiding mistakes; and the second in drawing to the attention of the public, modern nomenclature in the matter of units and numbers.

But eternal vigilance is necessary. The following are some mistakes which have occurred in recent years in newspaper reports, including several mistakes in the so-called 'Quality Press'. Using MW for mW or vice-versa are common errors. On more than one occasion an electrical power station costing millions of pounds to build has been stated to have an output of so-many milliwatts instead of megawatts! In a recent four-page special report on 'Metrication and Decimalization' a newspaper gave a yard as 0·914 4018 m (incorrect since 1963).

It is deplorable that several of the SI prefixes have been used in a qualitative sense; for example, references to 'mega-tons', meaning a great quantity. The term nanotechnology is being used more widely (1996) in descriptions of minute machines that will have applications in such techniques as surgery within blood vessels and organs. The use of SI prefixes in a quantitative sense however might be encouraged. Precision in language can help to eradicate the slipshod use of words which has now become all too common.

There might appear to be some inconsistencies in the matter of spelling in various parts of this text. In the UK, the original (French) spelling 'kilogramme' has been customary for the unit of mass. In the USA this word has habitually been written 'kilogram' and this is the alternative 'permitted' spelling in the UK according to several authoritative dictionaries. Correspondence between the National Physical Laboratory (UK) and the National Bureau of Standards (USA) has resulted in an agreement to the effect that whereas the spelling of this word in future publications of both bodies shall be in the form 'kilogram', there is also a recommendation that the spelling of the word 'litre' shall be retained in its French form, and that the American form 'liter' shall be discontinued. The change to 'kilogram' carries with it the change from gramme to gram, and correspondingly with all its multiples and sub-multiples.

Where 'kilogramme' appears in either of the two volumes of this book, it is generally in places where it seems appropriate such as in connection with the setting up in France of the original form of the metric system, and in some other places where this was the spelling customary at the time when decisions were being made concerning the unit of mass. Original spellings have been retained in most of the quotations reproduced in the text.

The United Nations book *World Weights and Measures* gave details of the bewildering array of units then in use throughout the world.[184] No fewer than 1680 different non-metric units were tabulated, many of them exhibiting the undesirable characteristics of the units that were prevalent until the end of the Middle Ages in Europe.

The decimal marker

A very unsatisfactory position has developed in relation to the notation for the decimal marker for decimal numbers. This situation is not the result of the introduction of metric units. The developing situation regarding international standardisation which has accompanied the widespread adoption of SI has merely served to bring the situation into greater prominence. It has also indicated the need for international agreement on this subject.

In the UK the traditional decimal marker has been for very many years a dot or point in the mid-figure position, thus: 25·4. The selection by the author and editor of Times roman as the type-face for this book was partly because the mid-point or raised decimal marker was available – not so for some other equally neat types. In most countries on the Continent of Europe and in the (former) USSR the decimal marker has been for many years a comma on the line, thus: 25,4. In the USA the decimal marker is a point on the line, thus: 25.4.

A most unusual notation was used by Richard Cumberland in his book[15] published in 1699. He uses as a decimal marker a comma, on the line but inverted, thus: 21ʻ888 to denote 21·888. Another unusual notation was used in 1721 by G Hooper.[13] He wrote 23·75 as 23$_c$75.

Writing in 1745; John Greaves, Professor of Astronomy at Oxford[14] used a comma as a decimal marker, as also did Samuel Reynardson, FRS, in 1750.[111]

George Collar[184] in his *Notes on the Metric System* – published in 1892 – used the decimal full point in the mid-position for an imperial quantity, thus: 39·37 inches; but for metric quantities he used the curious notation 45,^{m}305 to denote 45·305 metres, 57,^{km}047 for 57·047 kilometres, and 39,$^{sq.m}$4855 for 39·4855 square metres.

A common practice today (1996) is to denote an electrical resistor of, say, 4·7 ohms as 4R7.

When in the UK a start was made in industrial metrication, the British Standards Institution considered the problem arising from the use of the comma as a decimal marker in the main industrial countries that had been metric for many years. The construction industry was scheduled to be the first to achieve full metrication, and the Metric Panel for that industry set up by the BSI made a firm recommendation that in the UK we should follow Continental practice by using the decimal comma. A relevant point to be considered here was as follows: in the UK the traditional method (due to A S Leblond) of separating the groups of digits comprising very large numbers has been to use a comma to separate groups of three digits, thus:

9,781,283   1,257,000,000

In recent years this practice started to be replaced by the use of spaces between the groups of digits, thus:

9 781 283   1 257 000 000

Scientific and technical papers in particular have adopted this latter system, and in general the way seemed open to the introduction of the decimal comma. The BSI recommendation to the building industry to adopt the comma as a decimal marker failed to gain acceptance in practice, and the BSI dropped this recommendation.

The Decimal Currency Board which was set up by the Government to regulate the introduction of decimal money into the UK ignored the much more eminent bodies that have a permanent interest in the subject; and which were not just transient organisations like the Decimal Currency Board. This body decided that for monetary transactions the traditional decimal point (in the mid-position) should be used except on cheques when a hyphen must be used, and that commas should be used to separate groups of three digits in the case of long numbers. Thus on cheques, the symbolism for £34·15 must be £34-15. This, alas, now makes four possible styles for the decimal marker.

There is, unfortunately, no uniformity amongst the various bodies in the UK which exert strong influence in this matter of the decimal marker. The Symbols Committee of The Royal Society stated in its report that 'The decimal sign between digits in a number should be a point (·) or a comma (,). To facilitate the reading of long numbers the digits may be grouped in threes about the decimal sign but no point or comma should ever be used except for the decimal sign'.

Some people might regret the fact that there is in the UK no single authoritative body which can lay down a rule which everyone can follow. It would be much better for there to exist an international body which could command sufficient respect for its recommendations to be adhered to. In the fields of technology and commerce the International Standards Organisation is doing great work in the way of setting up standards which have almost world-wide recognition. The CGPM is also an international body with world-wide influence.

The need for international agreement on the symbol for the decimal marker is very urgent. All sorts of mistakes are made due to the lack of uniformity in practice. The figures 25,278 mean twenty five thousand two hundred and seventy eight to most people in the UK and to all those who follow the Decimal Currency Board practice; to most Continental people however, these figures mean twenty five point two seven eight, ie, a number one thousandth of the UK interpretation. Some time ago a newspaper reported that the surplus of foreign currency earned by the Norwegian merchant fleet was 370 million pounds, which was 35 400 million more than in the previous year! In this case the Continental symbolism for 35·4 million pounds increase was mistaken by the newspaper for 35 400 millions. This is only one of many such errors in the interpretation of numbers involving a decimal marker.

When the time comes for a definite recommendation to be made for world-wide acceptance, many difficulties will be encountered. Consider first the use of the traditional UK symbolism, a dot in the mid-position eg 47·138. In the UK there would be no mistake in the interpretation of this type of sign, although in a few other countries the meaning would be 'multiplied by', ie 47×138. As implied previously, the main disadvantage of the dot in the mid-position is the fact that many printers' type faces do not have this as a separate sign. The fact is that the dot on the line (the traditional full-stop) is being used more and more in typed work, and often copied thus in subsequent printed work.

Consider next the use of the point or dot on the line, eg 47.138. Its main advantage is the fact that all typewriters and word processors have this for use as a full stop at the end of a sentence. Another point in its favour is the fact that it is used extensively in the USA. As previously indicated, there are places however, where its meaning is 'multiply by'. In some countries the full point has been used as a separator for groups of three digits in long numbers, thus: 2.356.789 represents the same number as 2,356,789 in the traditional UK notation, or 2 356 789 in the modern notation.

The Continental use of a comma thus: 47,138 is likely to be advocated strongly when discussions take place at the international level. Its obvious disadvantage in the UK and in the USA is that the example shown above will be mistaken for forty seven thousand one hundred and thirty eight, instead of its intended meaning of forty seven point one three eight. It is not a complete answer to this difficulty to state that the new notation for separating the groups of digits in large number will render this misunderstanding unlikely. There is already in existence such an enormous volume of scientific and technical literature that mistakes and misinterpretations are bound to arise, and in any case it will take many years before the new notation of spaces instead of commas becomes universal practice. This criticism applies, of course, to all the previous methods of notation considered. What would really be the most desirable development would be the universal acceptance of an entirely new symbol for the decimal marker.

Proposals for a new decimal marker

There is a symbol which is worthy of consideration in this context. Consider the use of the semicolon, thus: 47;138. In the proposal being put forward here for an agreed symbol for the decimal marker, the advocates of the comma have got it, the advocates of the dot or full-point also have it. The fact that the symbol is a completely new one in this context eliminates the misunderstandings which are inevitable with the continued use of either the comma or the dot. There are other advantages in using a semicolon for the decimal marker. All typewriters and word processors have this symbol and moreover, it is a base symbol not requiring the use of the shift key to type it. On existing stencils, tracings and other types of reproducing equipment, the change would not involve any erasure where the equipment had the old symbolism and was going to be used again; with the comma on the line it merely needs the addition of a point or dot in the mid-position and in the case of the dot in the mid-position the addition of a comma on the line would complete the symbol. With a dot on the line the full semicolon symbol can be impressed without making any erasure. An additional advantage is that there would be no need for the symbol on cheques to differ from the symbol used for general accountancy. It is a distinct advantage that the proposed symbol is new for this purpose, and is not in general use for other mathematical purposes as is the dot or the colon. As a matter of interest, the proposal to use a semicolon for the decimal marker was first put forward by A S Leblond in 1798; although this proposal was not adopted, his other proposal that a comma should be used to separate groups of three digits in long numbers was adopted both in the UK and in the USA.

There seems to be one other relatively simple possibility for a brand new decimal marker should it be impossible to obtain support for the above proposal. This would be to use a hyphen, thus: 43 278-52.

The hyphen is also one available on all ordinary typewriters and word processors and can be typed without the use of the shift key. It is the symbol that would show up best in handwriting: it is not one used except on cheques in the UK. Occasionally it might be found when indicating upper and lower limits of some quantity, such as 57–96 [or 57 – 96] meaning 'between 57 and 96', but in this case there would normally be a pair of spaces between numbers, in addition to the hyphen. In most cases the context in which the numbers and characters occur would obviate confusion.

There are probably other possible symbols for the decimal marker worthy of consideration. The main point to realise is the urgency of some international agreement on this matter.

The publications of the National Physical Laboratory show decimal values with the point on the line. This custom also applies to the publications of the British Standards Institution except where the specification is in exact agreement with the corresponding publication of the International Standards Organisation. In such a case the ISO practice predominates, and a comma is used for the decimal marker. The following important document is an example of this.

BS 5775 1982 incorporating ISO 31/0–1981 includes the following statements.[183]

(a) Deviation from former British Standards: the comma has been used throughout as a decimal marker.

(b) To facilitate the reading of numbers with many digits, these may be separated into suitable groups, preferably of three, counting from the decimal sign towards the left and the right, the groups should be separated by a small space but never by a comma, a point or by other means.

(c) The preferred decimal sign is a comma on the line. If a dot is used, it shall be on the line.

(d) In accordance with an ISO Council decision the decimal sign is a comma in ISO documents.

(e) If a dot half-high is used as the multiplication sign, a comma should be used as the decimal sign. If a dot is used as a decimal sign an × should be used as a multiplication sign.

Computer programmers also have their conventions and these should not be allowed to sway any decision on standardisation that is advocated for general use. The urgency of a decision concerning the decimal marker is illustrated by the use of both the comma and the point on the line in different contexts in the *Official Journal of the European Community*. The advent of SI and also the extended use of the recommended prefixes for numbers widens the scope for the avoidance of the use of the decimal marker in many practical cases. In the building industry for example, where the degree of precision required by the work involved is not really high, an almost complete elimination of decimal parts in dimensions is being achieved by the choice of the millimetre as the unit of length on working drawings.

Meteorologists make extensive use of the millibar for quantifying atmospheric pressure and hence avoid decimal parts of the bar.

Motor vehicle fuel consumption

In the UK the 'petrol consumption' of a motor vehicle has been usually specified in terms of 'miles per gallon'. Strictly speaking 'gallons per mile' would be the correct sequence of words to denote fuel consumption. An advertisement for a gadget for a motor car to improve its performance stated that in a test 'fuel consumption fell from 29·1 mpg to 32·85 mpg' at a certain steady speed.

The idea of something *falling* from 29 to 32 seems somewhat whimsical. What has fallen, of course, is the number of gallons consumed per mile. In metric countries this method of appraisal is always used; the fuel consumption is given in litres per 100 kilometres travelled. Some typical figures given in Table XXVI indicate the order of magnitude of the metric type of specification for some values met with in practice.

Table XXVI
Fuel consumption equivalents (values rounded)

miles per UK gallon	10	20	30	40	50
litres per 100 km	28	14	9½	7	5½

Since there is a big difference between the UK gallon and the USA gallon [ratio 6:5], a separate table is necessary for the latter measure of capacity.

Table XXVII
Fuel consumption equivalents (values rounded)

miles per USA gallon	10	20	30	40	50
litres per 100 km	23½	11¾	8	6	4¾

Surviving non-metric units as at 1909–10 and 1926–27

The survival on the Continent of Europe of certain old non-metric units, usually in remote country districts, is sometimes cited as evidence

TABLE 36.—WEIGHTS AND MEASURES OF DIFFERENT COUNTRIES.

1. **Metric System** (compulsory in France, Germany, Austria, the Netherlands, Belgium, Luxemburg, Switzerland, Italy, Greece, Turkey, Roumania, Spain, Portugal, and most of the South American Republics; optional in Great Britain, the United States, and Russia).

1 metre (m.) = 443·296 Paris lignes = 3·280899 English feet = 3·18620 Prussian feet = 1·00000301 metre des archives.

1 kilometre (km.) = 10 hectometres (hm.) = 0·6214 English mile = 0·1328 Prussian mile = 0·9375 Russian verst = 0·5390 nautical mile = 0·1347 geographical mile (15 to 1 degree of longitude).

1 lieue (France) = 1 myriametre = 10 km.

1 German mile = 7½ km. = 0·996 Prussian mile = 4·66 English miles.

1 hectare (ha.) = 100 ares (a.) = 10,000 sq.m. = 0·01 sq.km. = 2·471 English acres.

1 litre (l.) = 0·001 cb.m. = 1000 c.cm. = 0·2201 gallon.

1 hectolitre (hl.) = 0·1 cb.m. = 100 l. = 22·01 gallons.

1 kilogram (kg.) = 1000 g. = weight of 1 litre of water at + 4° C. = 2 German and Swiss pounds (zollpfund) = 0·999999842 kilogram prototype = 2·2046 pounds avoirdupois = 1·7857 Austrian pounds = 2·3511 Swedish pounds = 2·4419 Russian pounds.

1 gram (g.) = 15·432 grains (English).

1 quintal = 100 kg. = 196·84 lbs. avoirdupois = 1 cwt. 3 qr. 0·84 lb.

1 metrical ton = 1000 kg. = 0·9842 English ton = 1·023 American short tons (at 2000 lbs.).

2. **Great Britain and Ireland.**

1 foot = 0·3047943 m.

1 inch = 25·3995 mm.

1 yard = 0·9143835 m.

1 fathom = 2 yards.

1 rod (pole, perch) = 5½ yards = 5·029109 m.

1 statute mile = 8 furlongs = 320 poles = 1760 yards = 5280 feet = 1·6093 kilometre (km.).

1 nautical mile = ₆₀th degree (at the equator). 6082·66 feet = 1854·96 m.

1 acre = 4 roods = 160 poles = 0·40467 ha. = 43,560 square feet = 4047 square metres.

1 square mile = 640 acres = 259·0 ha.

1 gallon = 4 quarts = 8 pints = 277·274 cubic inches = 4·536 litres.

1 cubic foot = 28·3153 l.

1 cubic inch = 16·3862 c.cm.

1 quarter = 8 bushels = 32 pecks = 64 gallons = 2·903 hl.

1 bushel = 8 gallons = 0·3628 hl.

1 fluid ounce = ₂₀th pint = 28·35 c.cm.

1 pound avoirdupois (lb.) = 16 ounces (oz.) = 7000 grains = 0·4535926 kg.

1 ounce avoirdupois = 437½ grains = 28·35 g.

1 gallon = 10 lbs. water = 70,000 grains = 4·535926 kg. water.

1 hundredweight (cwt.) = 4 quarters (qr.) = 8 stones = 112 lbs. = 50·8024 kg.

1 ton = 20 cwt. = 2240 lbs. = 1016·648 kg.

Apothecaries' Weight.

1 pound troy = 12 ounces troy = 96 drams = 288 scruples = 5760 grains = 373·24195 g.

1 ounce troy = 8 drams = 24 scruples = 480 grains = 31·1035 g.

1 ounce troy (for gold and precious stones) = 20 pennyweight (dwt.) = 480 grains = 31·1035 g.

1 grain (common to avoirdupois and troy weight) = 0·06479895 g.

Figure 34 – Pages from The Technical Chemists' Handbook (Lunge, 1910, Gurney and Jackson).[190]

3. Austria (old measures and weights, now abolished for the metric system).

1 foot = 0·316102 m., at 12 inches of 12 lines each.
3 ruthen = 5 klafter = 30 feet = 360 zoll.
1 meile = 4000 klafter = 7586·455 m.
1 maass = 1·415 l.
1 eimer = 40 maass = 160 seidel.
1 metze = 61·4995 l.
1 Wiener pfund = 560·012 g.
1 centner = 5 stein = 100 pfund = 3200 loth.

4. Denmark and Norway employ, as unit of measure, the Prussian foot, as unit of weight the units of the metrical system, viz., kilos, etc.

5. Prussia (old system, now abolished for the metric system).

1 foot (Rhenish foot) = 12 zoll (inches) = 144 linien = 0·313853 m.
1 ruthe = 12 fuss = 3·76624 m.
1 lachter (fathom) = 80 zoll = 2·09326 m.
1 meile = 24,000 fuss = 7532·5 m.
1 morgen = 180 square ruthen = 0·2553 ha.
1 quart = 64 cubic inches = $\frac{1}{7}$ cubic foot = 1·14503 l.
1 scheffel = 16 Metzen = 48 quarts = 0·54961 hl.
1 tonne = 4 scheffel = 2·19846 hl.
1 klafter = 108 cubic fuss = 3·3389 cb.m.
1 schachtruthe = 144 cubic fuss = 4·4519 cb.m.
1 pfund = 30 loth = 300 quentchen = 500 g.
1 centner = 100 pfund = 50 kg.   (Formerly 1 pfund = 32 loth = 467·711 g. ; 1 centner = 110 pfund.)

6. Russia.

1 foot = 1 English foot.
1 sashehn = 7 feet = 3 arshin = 12 tchetvert = 48 vershok = 2·13357 m.
1 verst = 500 sashehn = 1066·78 m.
1 dessatine = 2400 square sashehns = 10925 m.
1 vedro = 10 krushky (stoof) = 12·299 l.
1 tchetvert = 1 osmini = 4 payok = 8 tchetverik = 209·9 l.
1 pound = 32 loth = 96 solotnik = 9216 doli = 0·9028 Eng. lb. = 409·531 g.
1 berkovets = 10 pud = 400 pounds = 163·81 kg.
1 pud = 40 pounds = 36·112 Eng. lb. = 16·3805 kg.

7. Sweden.

1 foot = 10 zoll (inches) = 100 lines = 0·97408 Eng. foot = 0·296901 m.
1 famn (fathom) = 3 alnar (ells) = 6 feet = 5·58445 Eng. feet = 1·7814 m.
1 mile = 6000 fathoms = 6·6417 Eng. statute miles = 10·6884 km.
1 kanne = 100 cubic inches = 0·57694 Eng. gallon = 2·617 l.
1 skalpund = 100 korn (at 100 art) = 0·9378 Eng. lb. = 425·3395 g.
1 centner = 100 skalpund.
1 skipspund = 20 liespund = 400 skalpund.

8. Switzerland. Metrical measure and weight. The following are sometimes still employed :—

1 fuss = 0·3000 m. = 0·9843 Eng. foot.
1 juchart = 36 are = 0·88956 Eng. acre.
1 maass = 1·51 l.
1 saum = 100 maass = 151 l.

9. United States. Weights and measures as in Great Britain, but instead of the " long ton " (gross ton) of 2240 lb., more frequently the " short ton " (net ton) of 2000 lbs. = 907·1852 kg. = 0·89285 long ton, is employed.

Figure 34a.

that the metric system has not been fully adopted after many years of metric-oriented legislation. Two 'snapshots' from the early part of the 20th century are instructive. Professor George Lunge of Zurich Federal Polytechnic in 1909–10 published *The Technical Chemists' Handbook*.[190] Pages from this book are reproduced here (Figure 34).

A little later, in the years 1926–27 Professor A E Kennelly, then at Harvard, made a tour of Europe (excluding Scandinavia) for the purpose of ascertaining the extent to which pre-metric weights and measures had persisted in metric countries. His main finding was that the greatest incidence of pre-metric units was in documents relating to land tenure and registry. This should not be surprising since such documents tend to be required mostly in connection with deaths and with the sale of estates, and these naturally occur less frequently than the sale of everyday commodities. *In toto*, the number of cases where pre-metric units were still in use was relatively small. He distinguished between three different types of case involving non-metric usage.

(a)   The use of a residual unit occuring in concrete form as a non-metric standard and hence completely non-metric.

(b)   The use of old unit values and names from an earlier system but which were always measured in practice with metric scales or weights; he called these sub-metricised units.

(c)   The use of an old name for a quantity which is clearly a metric quantity; he called these 'metricised units'.

The number of cases in category (a) was quite small. In some parts of Germany the Rheinischer Zoll (Rhineland inch) was still being used, its value being 3·615 cm, but the same name was also being used for a unit being measured with metric tapes and rules. The 'English inch' was being used in connection with Whitworth screw threads, glove sizes, shoe sizes and stocking sizes. In Majorca, silver ornaments were being made and sold by weight using a completely non-metric system and using non-metric weights of the following denominations:

The smallest unit was the gramos, equal to 0·0589 gramme. The multiples were:

36 gramos	=	1 adarme	(2·12 grammes)
4 adarmes	=	1 cuarto	(8·48 grammes)
4 cuartos	=	1 onza	(33·9 grammes)
12 onzas	=	1 libra	(407 grammes)

This was the sum total units still in use in 1927 that were completely non-metric. [But see Lunge for units in use in 1909: two pages of the book are reproduced in Figure 34 – Ed.][190]

The number of units in category (b) was greater but were sometimes trade terms for specific commercial quantities which had been found convenient in the past. Amongst these were

aune: used for the measurement of textiles, and corresponding to the medieval 'ell' in Britain. In Holland and Belgium the size of this unit was 70 centimetres which was the metricised value of the original aune which varied between 67 cm and 73 cm according to district. In France it could be either 120 cm in length or 114 cm, again according to the district in which it was found.

pounce: used in parts of Germany to denote an area of agricultural land. It was supposed to be originally the area of land that could be ploughed in a morning. Its value in Prussia was 2553 m^2, in Wurtenberg 3152 m^2 and Baden 3600 m^2. A corresponding idea persisted in Bavaria where the Tagwerk (day's work) was equal to 3407 m^2. In Austria the Joch was equal to 5755 m^2.

libbra: found in some parts of Italy, was a unit of weight almost equal to one third of a kilogramme.

In category (c) full metricised units with old names were being used on a wider scale than any of the units in the two previous categories. It was, for example, much more common to find the Morgen and Tagwerk in Germany equal to 2500 m^2 exactly. In France the old unit of length called the 'toise' was 2 metres, and the 'pied' (foot) equal to one-third of a metre. The livre of 500 grammes exactly was very widespread in European countries using the French language. In some parts of France the 'pinte' was a popular name for one litre.

A position similar to that described above is likely to arise in the United Kingdom after full metrication. The EEC Directives on Metrication do not apply outside the realms of industry and commerce. Thus in the field of sport, imperial units can be retained. This was

made clear in a consultation paper on the use of metric units issued
in 1988 by the Department of Trade and Industry.

It is likely that many adults will retain their figures for body weight
in the old form, in accordance with the general reluctance of people
to change ingrained habits: see Table XXVIII.

Table XXVIII			
Table of equivalent body weights			
UK style	6 stone	7 stone	7 stone 12 lb
USA style	84 lb	98 lb	110 lb
metric	38 kg	44 kg	50 kg
UK style	8 stone 7 lb	10 stone 10 lb	12 stone
USA style	119 lb	150 lb	168 lb
metric	54 kg	68 kg	76 kg
UK style	14 stone	16 stone	17 stone 12 lb
USA style	196 lb	224 lb	250 lb
metric	89 kg	102 kg	113 kg

Large numbers, inconsistencies and pronunciation

The more widespread use of SI prefixes can bring several advantages
in the matter of understanding numerical values of all kinds. There is
no need to confine the use of the agreed SI prefixes for large and
small numbers to metric quantities. Great benefit in the way of clarity
and precision in communication will arise from a more widespread
use of these prefixes in other directions. Thus the muddle concerning
the use of the words 'billion' and 'trillion' can be eliminated by
dropping these words altogether and using the approriate SI prefixes.
In 1948 the CGPM adopted for international use the convention as in
Table XXIX.

Table XXIX		
Large numbers, UK convention		
term		corresponding power
million	thousand × thousand	10^6
billion	million × million	10^{12}
trillion	million × billion	10^{18}
quadrillion	million × trillion	10^{24}

The greatest confusion has arisen because in the USA the convention is quite different. Although the 'million' is the same, the other terms are as in Table XXX.

Table XXX		
Large numbers, USA convention		
term		corresponding power
billion	thousand × million	10^9
trillion	million × million	10^{12}
quadrillion	million × US billion	10^{15}

Difficulties started to arise in the United Kingdom when newspaper reports appearing in American papers were copied directly by UK newspapers without thought as to the UK meaning attributable to the words 'billion' and 'trillion'. The application of the agreed SI prefixes for money reports would be quite simple and would clarify the situation and remove ambiguity.

The present style of writing the symbols for money is unsound. When a reader sees for example '£2m' his natural inclination is to say mentally 'two pounds million'; a BBC announcer on Radio 4 once said precisely that.

The practice of writing £5 for five pounds is illogical and was not always the custom in England. There are many documents from the Middle Ages where money values were written with the pound sign after the numeric. In the archives of the Portsmouth City Records Office is a document dated 1632 showing the sum of '639£ 11s' in relation to Bedhampton Manor. In 1770 Edmund Burke wrote to a friend asking for a loan of '1500£'. It does not seem possible to specify a date when the practice of writing quantities of the pound sterling changed to present practice. There is evidence that the pound sign before the numeric had been the custom as early as 1660. Both methods of specifying pound sterling quantities in the same document was quoted by William Fallows in the correspondence column of *The Times* (4 November 1989); in the *Tutor's Assistant* written by Francis Walkingame, the 1797 edition for which the publishers had engaged a Mr Crosby to work every question anew 'so that many errors were expunged'. However, in the questions the five pounds is written as 5*l*, but in the answers as £5.

Prior to decimalisation of the coinage in the UK in 1971, sums of money were written in terms of pounds, shillings and pence. The symbolism for such an amount as two pounds, five shilling and nine pence was £2 5s 9d. This custom was derived from the time when amounts of money were written in Latin; the letters standing for *librae, solidi* and *denarii*. Gradually with the decline of Latin the abbreviation *l* was superseded by the symbol £; this sign was in the nature of an abbreviation. Since s and d both were written after the numeric, it does not seem logical that the symbol £ should precede the numeric.

Consider the amount of money usually specified by £5m, meaning five million pounds. For science-based people the small 'm' means 'milli' but it is intended to mean 'million' for which the symbol should be 'M'. This is the SI prefix for mega, so why not think of the above quantity as 'five megapounds' and use the symbol 5M£?

The American quantity one billion pounds would be 1000M£ or 1G£ (one gigapound): think of 'gigantic pound'. This suggestion for specifying the quantity 'one thousand million pounds' is put forward to avoid confusion over the word billion which is used in the USA for this quantity. This could have been avoided by the use of the word 'milliard' (10^9) but the widespread neglect of the use of this designation renders change necessary: the word 'billion' should be abolished. In a letter to *Nature* (18 June 1971) Dr Kenneth Mellanby of Monks Wood Experimental Station pleaded for the abolition of the use of the word billion, in the interest of scientific accuracy.

In the United Kingdom a billion has traditionally been equal to a million million, ie 1 000 000 000 000, or 10^{12}. This has corresponded to practice in Germany, France, Holland, Denmark, Norway, Spain (billion), Sweden and even in the Welsh language (biliwn). During the hyper-inflation in Germany after World War I the banknote of value one million million marks was designated 'Eine Billion' (one billion) marks. After World War II in the Hungarian hyper-inflation of 1945–46 a billion pengo (bilpengo) was a million million pengo.

The SI prefix for a million million or 10^{12} is tera and its symbol is T. The word 'tera' derives from the Greek word for monster. We thus denote a million million metres as a terametre, for which the symbol is Tm. The following further examples show how the UK billion would be eliminated. [Note: the figures are for illustrative purposes, and are only estimates -Ed.]

(a) The annual water consumption in the UK is about 2 million million gallons. This statement could be made to read that the stated water consumption is 2 teragallons. This is an interesting example because the UK gallon is 20% bigger than the USA gallon, which demonstrates the need for universal metrication. The completely unambiguous statement of the above fact would read: 'The stated water consumption is 9 teralitres (TL)'.

(b) In 1990 the Gross National Product of Japan was about 250 million million yen, ie 250 terayen.

(c) The number of cigarettes manufactured in the world in 1994 was estimated at 4 500 000 million. This could be expressed as 4·5 teracigarettes.

In the case of the prefix giga there is no universal agreement concerning its pronunciation in the English language. In origin it comes from the Latin word for giant and is the source of the word 'gigantic'. There are six possible variants in pronunciation but only three have been used to any extent in practice. The least common pronunciation makes both gs hard; the nearest common word to describe this is 'giggle' (laughter). It seems unlikely that this particular style of pronunciation will find wide acceptance.

The pronunciation that has been used amongst telecommunication engineers also has both gs pronounced hard. The phonetic signs used in the *Oxford English Dictionary* would give g-iga. The suggestion given above for giga is the only one about which there is likely to be different opinions.

The third style of pronunciation of giga is the one strongly recommended by the present author. The key to this lies in the everyday pronunciation of the word 'gigantic' which obviously has the same roots. Some would write this pronunciation as jé-ga. The National Bureau of Standards (USA) writes the pronunciation as 'ji'ga' which also makes clear the soft pronunciation of the first g and the hard pronunciation of the second g. *Chambers Dictionary* gives the pronunciation of giga as 'jyga as in gigantic'.

Summing up, therefore, we can avoid the use of the word billion, particularly in money matters, and express large values in terms of the internationally agreed prefixes tera and giga.

It might be thought that since the USA billion is one thousand times a million there should be no confusion in practice. This is not the case and mistakes are still being made. A BBC announcer on Radio 4, reporting on a major project initiated by the United States Government, gave the estimated cost as three million dollars. He then hesitated and said, 'this must be three billion dollars'. He was probably right in making this verbal correction of his written manuscript since 3 000 000 dollars would be small in an American budget.

A Nation-wide TV broadcast on BBC 1 in 1976 reported that since the Bank of England used the word 'billion' to denote a thousand million as in the USA, then the BBC would use the word billion for the same numerical value. In 1975 the Press Council had rejected, as an exercise in pedantry, a complaint that *The Times* had refused to publish a letter criticising the use of the word billion. This perhaps shows how ill-informed was the Press Council.

Since all the bodies mentioned above are arts-dominated, it is not surprising that their competence in this matter is questionable. At the same time Dr G B R Feilden FRS, then Director General of the BSI stated that the use of the terms 'billion', 'trillion' and 'quadrillion' should be avoided. Even when there is no ambiguity as with the number 1000, there are occasions when it would be useful to refer to £1000 as 1k£ (one kilopound). Advertisements for scientific staff in the electronics industry frequently specify the salary in the following way: £14k which means £14 000 per annum; sometimes one might read £14K, meaning the same thing.

There is another term, fortunately very rare, which has different meanings in different countries. The word 'decillion' has been used in the past with the following meanings: 10^{33} in the USA and in France, but 10^{60} in the UK and in Germany.

During World War II the large number of American personnel brought with them to the UK their own particular pronunciation of the word 'kilometre' ('kilometer' in the USA). Their pronunciation approximates to 'kil'omitr' which loses completely the two essential components of the word viz 'kilo' meaning 'a 1000 times' and 'metre' meaning the unit of the length concerned.

There seems to have been a false analogy between this pronunciation and that of words like thermometer and barometer. In the former the basic word is 'therm' and in the latter the root word is 'bar'. The letter 'o' is inserted purely for euphony and has no meaning in itself. In the case of the word 'kilometre', both the l and the o are essential parts of the prefix. It is illogical therefore, to merge this part of the prefix with the stem denoting the unit. Further, it should be noted that words like 'thermometer' and barometer' are qualitative; that is, they are descriptive. By way of contrast, the word 'kilometre' is quantitative and very precisely so; it means 1000 metres exactly.

Attempts have been made to justify the American pronunciation by quoting the emphasis on the ancient Greek word for 1000. This is quite unsound; the prefix 'kilo' is a term coined by the French and has little resemblance to the Greek word 'chilio' meaning 1000.

For a word with which one is not familiar such as kilobyte, kilohertz, kilojoule; it is good advice to subtract the prefix kilo-: then consult a suitable dictionary to find the meaning of the stem word.

It would be a good idea if in teaching at the elementary stage an old practice came into use again. In this primary stage, a word with a prefix could be written with a hyphen between the prefix and the stem. This would give for example deci-metre, hecto-litre, mega-gram, kilo-metre, and so on. The hyphen would be dropped at a later stage in the teaching. In the UK, metric units have been taught in schools for over 90 years but this is not the case in the USA, except for science studies. It is, therefore, unsound practice for Britain to take its pronunciation of this word from the USA's rendition.

If we could gather together the politicians of the world in the same spirit that has enabled scientists and technologists to frame a common language for international communication in the matter of units and rules for weights and measures, world peace might be much nearer. Understanding starts with precise language. If politicians would get together to frame precise definitions of, say, colonialism, democracy, socialism, communism and terrorism, and agree to use these words only with those precise meanings, the many sides relative to their ideologies would have started to understand one another the better.

A final note, and remarks about the Appendices

The various Tables that follow in the Appendices need little justification, since they are included to assist readers in comprehending less familiar units. There are also information and data that was deemed to be desirable in the publication, but did not conveniently fit into the main text, for example Appendix F on pH and the brief commentary on dimensional analysis Appendix H.

The specialist may regret that his particular subject has been overlooked or treated superficially. He or she is referred to Appendix J.

Some material that was written has been discarded in favour of copy that has been considered more pressing. For example, the author wrote a chapter on the history of electrical units, but this has been omitted due to pressure on space. On due reflection, the reader will appreciate that selection of material is a subjective matter. We, author and editor, have aimed to please as far as we have been able.

Both the author and editor of these two volumes have been practicing professionals in both industry and education throughout their working lives. During their combined total of some ninety years of such experience they have also come to appreciate that life itself is a school of learning, and the basis of good measuring practice is to treat every result with due caution.

For this reason Appendix J has been included in this book.

Appendix A1

Definitions of the base units and supplementary units of SI (The international system of units)

Unit of length

metre [symbol m]: The metre is the length of the path travelled by light in vacuum during a time interval of 1/299 792 458 of a second. [17th CGPM (1983), Resolution 1]

Unit of mass

kilogram [symbol kg]: The kilogram is the unit of mass; it is equal to the mass of the international prototype of the kilogram.
[3rd CGPM (1901)] *Note: this is the only SI unit still defined by means of a physical artifact or material standard.*

Unit of time

second [symbol s]: The second is the duration of 9 192 631 770 periods of the radiation corresponding to the transition between the two hyperfine levels of the ground state of the caesium–133 atom. [13th CGPM (1967), Resolution 1]

Unit of electrical current

ampere [symbol A]: The ampere is that constant current which, if maintained in two straight parallel conductors of infinite length, of negligible circular cross-section, and placed 1 metre apart in vacuum, would produce between these conductors a force equal to 2×10^{-7} newton per metre of length.
[CIPM (1946), Resolution 2 approved by the 9th CGPM (1948)]

Unit of thermodynamic temperature (T) and interval of difference in temperature (t or °C)

kelvin [symbol K]: The kelvin, unit of thermodynamic temperature, is the fraction 1/273·16 of the thermodynamic temperature of the triple point of water. [13th CGPM (1967), Resolution 4 & Resolution 3]

Unit of amount of substance

mole [symbol mol]: The mole is the amount of substance of a system which contains as many elementary entities as there are atoms in 0·012 kilogram of carbon–12. When the mole is used, the elementary entities must be specified and may be atoms, molecules, ions, electrons, other particles, or specified groups of such particles.
[14th CGPM (1971), Resolution 3]

Unit of luminous intensity

candela [symbol cd]: The candela is the luminous intensity, in a given direction, of a source that emits monochromatic radiation of frequency 540×10^{12} hertz and that has a radiant intensity in that direction of 1/683 watt per steradian.
[18th CGPM (1979), Resolution 3]

Supplementary units of SI

Unit of plane angle

radian [symbol rad]: The radian is that angle subtended at the centre of a circle by an arc of length equal to its radius.
[2π radians = 360°, 1 radian = 57·296°]

Unit of solid angle

steradian [symbol sr]: The steradian is that solid angle which would just enclose a spherical area on the surface of a sphere such that the area is equal to the square of the radius of the sphere from which centre the angle is constructed.

Appendix A2

Table of SI prefixes

	Factors by which the unit is multiplied			
prefix	*words*	*index*	*symbol*	*pronunciation*
yotta	one million-million-million-million	10^{24}	Y	yotta
zetta	one thousand-million-million-million	10^{21}	Z	zetta
exa	one million-million-million	10^{18}	E	exa
peta	one thousand-million-million	10^{15}	P	peta (as in petal)
tera	one million-million	10^{12}	T	terra
giga	one thousand-million	10^{9}	G	jyga (as in gigantic)
mega	one million	10^{6}	M	megga
kilo	one thousand	10^{3}	k	killoh
hecto	one hundred	10^{2}	h	hektoh
deca	ten	10^{1}	da	decka
deci	one tenth	10^{-1}	d	dessie
centi	one hundredth	10^{-2}	c	sen tee
milli	one thousandth	10^{-3}	m	millie
micro	one millionth	10^{-6}	μ	mike/roh
nano	one thousand-millionth	10^{-9}	n	nannoh
pico	one million-millionth	10^{-12}	p	peakoh
femto	one thousand-million-millionth	10^{-15}	f	femtoh
atto	one million-million-millionth	10^{-18}	a	attoh
zepto	one thousand-million-million-millionth	10^{-21}	z	zeptoe
yocto	one million-million-million-millionth	10^{-24}	y	yoctoe

Appendix B

Notes on conversion tables

1. It would undoubtedly be very convenient to have for everyday purposes a unit of capacity (volume) equal to 1 cubic decimetre and named the litre. Unfortunately this relationship cannot be used when very precise measurements are involved. By definition the litre is the volume of 1 kilogramme of pure water at normal atmospheric pressure and maximum density. In the early days of the metric system this could be equated with a volume of 1 cubic decimetre. Modern measurements give the litre as defined above a volume equal to $1.000\ 028\ dm^3$. By a resolution of the twelfth CGPM in 1964 the word 'litre' is recognised as a special name for the cubic decimetre but must not be used to express the results of measurements of high precision. It is for this reason that in the following tables values of volume and capacity are given in both dm^3 and litres where these differ. In general one can use the litre and the millilitre for $1\ dm^3$ and $1\ cm^3$ respectively when the desired degree of precision is not better than 1 in 20 000.

2. In connection with moment of intertia it should be noted that in some European Continental countries, use is made of md^2 instead of mr^2. Since the diameter d is twice the radius r, the former expression is four times the magnitude of the customary quantity in the UK and the USA.

3. Where 'calorie' or 'kilocalorie' is stated without any suffix, this means the international calorie, or its multiple.

4. In connection with 'volume rate of flow' the customary word for the British unit, cubic foot per second, is 'cusec'. The practice of calling the corresponding metric unit, cubic metre per second, 'cumec' is to be deprecated.

5. When the c.g.s. system was in common use, the negative index was obviated by employing the solidus or negative stroke, as in cm/s^2 for acceleration. However ambiguities arose when more than one solidus was used. Consequently negative indices are preferred: the SI unit for acceleration becomes cm s^{-2}.

Conversion Table B1

SI and c.g.s. coherent units (non-electrical)

(all these are exact relationships)

physical quantity	*symbol*	*c.g.s. unit*	*abbreviation*	*value in SI units*
length	l	centimetre	cm	10^{-2} m
area	A	square centimetre	cm^2	10^{-4} m^2
volume	V	cubic centimetre	cm^3	10^{-6} m^3
capacity	V	litre (see Note 1, p366)	l	10^{-3} m^3
mass	m	gram	g	10^{-3} kg
mass per unit length	m/l	gram per centimetre	g/cm	10^{-1} kg m^{-1}
mass per unit area	m/A	gram per square centimetre	g/cm^2	10 kg m^{-2}
mass density	d	gram per cubic centimetre	g/cm^3	10^3 kg m^{-3}
specific volume	v	cubic centimetre per gram	cm^3/g	10^{-3} m^3 kg^{-1}
concentration	ρ	gram per litre (see Note 1, p366)	g/l	1 kg m^{-3}
velocity	u,v	centimetre per second	cm/s	10^{-2} m s^{-1}
volume rate of flow	V,Q	cubic centimetre per second	cm^3/s	10^{-6} m^3 s^{-1}
mass rate of flow	m/t	gram per second	g/s	10^{-3} kg s^{-1}
momentum	ρ	gram centimetre per second	g cm/s	10^{-5} kg m s^{-1}

physical quantity	symbol	c.g.s. unit	abbreviation	value in SI units
angular momentum	b or ρ	gram centimetre squared per second	g cm^2/s	10^{-7} kg m^2 s^{-1}
acceleration	a	Galileo (1 cm/s^2)	Gal	10^{-2} m s^{-2}
force	F	dyne	dyn	10^{-5} N
torque	T	dyne centimetre	dyn cm	10^{-7} Nm
power	P	erg per second	erg/s	10^{-7} W
pressure and stress	ρ σ	dyne per square centimetre (μbar)	dyn/cm^2	10^{-1} N m^{-2}
section modulus	Z	centimetre cubed	cm^3	10^{-6} m^3
second moment of area	I$_a$	centimetre to the fourth	cm^4	10^{-8} m^4
stiffness and surface tension	Y or σ	dyne per centimetre	dyn/cm	10^{-3} N m^{-1}
moment of inertia	J	gram centimetre squared	g cm^2	10^{-7} kg m^2
dynamic viscosity	χ or μ	poise	P	10^{-1} N s m^{-2}
kinematic viscosity	v	stokes	St	10^{-4} m^2 s^{-1}
specific energy	u or e	erg per gram	erg/g	10^{-4} J kg^{-1}
luminance	L	candela per square centimetre	cd/cm^2	10^4 nit
illumination	E	lumen per square centimetre	lm/cm^2	10^4 lx
sound energy flux	P	erg per second	erg/s	10^{-7} W
sound energy density		erg per cubic centimetre	erg/cm^3	10^{-1} J m^{-3}
sound intensity	I or J	erg per second per square centimetre	erg/s cm^2	10^{-3} W m^{-2}
acoustic impedance		ohm per square centimetre	Ω cm^{-2}	10^5 SI acoustic ohm

Conversion Table B1 (part 2)

SI and c.g.s. electrostatic units (e.s.u.) and electromagnetic units (e.m.u.)

For precise calculations substitute 2·997 924 58 for the numeral 3 in the e.s.u. list.

physical quantity		SI unit		value in e.s.u.	value in e.m.u.
length	l	1 metre	m	10^2 cm	10^2 cm
power	P	1 watt	W	10^7 erg s^{-1}	10^7 erg s^{-1}
potential difference	V	1 volt	V	$1/300$	10^8
current	I	1 ampere	A	3×10^9	10^{-1} biot
resistance	R	1 ohm	Ω	$(\frac{1}{3}^2) \times 10^{-11}$	10^9
resistivity		ohm metre		$(\frac{1}{3}^2) \times 10^{-9}$	10^{11}
current density	J	amp metre^{-2}		3×10^5	10^{-5}
quantity of electricity	Q	1 coulomb	C	3×10^9 franklin	10^{-1}
conductance		1 siemans	S	$3^2 \times 10^{11}$	10^{-9}
conductivity		siemans metre^{-1}		$3^2 \times 10^9$	10^{-11}
capacitance	C	1 farad	F	$3^2 \times 10^{11}$	10^{-9}
surface charge density		coulomb metre^{-2}		3×10^5	10^{-5}
volume charge density		coulomb metre^{-3}		3×10^3	10^{-7}
electrical flux	Q	coulomb		$4\pi \times 3 \times 10^9$	4×10^{-1}
electrical displacement	D	coulomb metre^{-2}		$4\pi \times 3 \times 10^5$	4×10^{-5}
electrical field strength	E	volt metre^{-1}		$(\frac{1}{3}) \times 10^{-4}$	10^6
electrical polarization	P	coulomb metre^{-2}		3×10^5	10^{-5}
electrical dipole moment	M	coulomb metre		3×10^{11}	10

physical quantity		SI unit		value in e.s.u.	value in e.m.u.
magnetic flux		1 weber	Wb	1/300	10^8 maxwell
magnetic flux density	B	1 tesla	T	$(\frac{1}{3}) \times 10^{-6}$	10^4 gauss
magnetic field intensity	H	1 amp metre^{-1}		$4 \times 3 \times 10^{-7}$	$4\pi \times 10^{-3}$ oersted
magneto-motive force	F_m	1 amp turn		$4 \times 3 \times 10^{-9}$	$4\pi \times 10^{-1}$ gilbert
self-inductance	L	1 henry	H	$(\frac{1}{3}^2) \times 10^{-11}$	10^9
mutual inductance	M	1 henry	H	$(\frac{1}{3}^2) \times 10^{-11}$	10^9
magnetic reluctance	R_m	amp weber^{-1}		$4\pi \times 3 \times 10^{11}$	$4\pi \times 3 \times 10^{-9}$ gilbert
permeance	P_m	weber amp^{-1}		$(\frac{1}{4}\pi) \times (\frac{1}{3}^2) \times 10^{-11}$	$(\frac{1}{4}\pi) \times 10^9$
magnetic potential	A	weber metre		$\frac{1}{3}$	10^{10} maxwell cm
magnetic pole strength		weber		$1/(4\pi \times 300)$	$(\frac{1}{4}\pi) \times 10^8$
magnetic area moment	m	amp metre^2		3×10^{13}	10^3
magnetic di-pole moment	j	weber metre		$(\frac{1}{4}\pi) \times (\frac{1}{3})$	$(\frac{1}{4}\pi) \times 10^{10}$
magnetization	M	amp metre^{-1}		3×10^7	10^{-3}
magnetic polarization	J	1 tesla	T	$(\frac{1}{4}\pi) \times \frac{1}{3} \times 10^{-6}$	$(\frac{1}{4}\pi) \times 10^4$

Conversion Table B2

SI and metric technical units

(these are exact relationships except where marked *)

physical quantity	*symbol*	*metric technical unit*	*abbreviation*	*value in SI units*
length	L	metre	m	unity
mass	m	hyl	hyl	9·806 65 kg
mass density		hyl per cubic metre	hyl/m^3	9·806 65 kg m^{-3}
momentum		kilopond second	kgf s	9·806 65 N s
angular momentum		metre kilopond second	m kgf s	9·806 65 kg m^2 s
force	F	kilogram force or kilopond	kgf or kp	9·806 65 N
energy		kilopond metre	kgf m	9·806 65 J
		kilocalorie	kcal	4·1868 kJ
torque	T	kilopond metre	kgf m	9·806 65 N m
power		kilopond metre per second	kgf m/s	9·806 65 W
		metric horsepower	PS (German) CV (French)	735·499 W *
pressure		kilopond per square metre	kgf/m^2	9·806 65 N m^{-2}
		millimetre of water	mm H_2O	9·806 65 N m^{-2}
		kilopond per square centimetre	kgf/cm^2	98 066·5 N m^{-2}
		kilopond per square millimetre	kgf/mm^2	9·806 65 MN m^{-2}
stiffness		kilopond per metre	kgf/m	9·806 65 N m^{-1}
surface tension		kilopond per metre	kgf/m	9·806 65 N m^{-1}

physical quantity	*symbol*	*metric technical unit*	*abbreviation*	*value in SI units*
moment of inertia	J	hyl metre-squared (see Note 2)	hyl m^2	9·806 65 kg m^2
dynamic viscosity	η	kilopond second per square metre	kgfs/m^2	9·806 65 N s m^{-2}
kinematic viscosity	μ	metre-squared per second	m^2/s	unity
calorific value (volume)		kilocalorie per cubic metre	kcal/m^3	4·1868 kJ m^{-3}
specific energy		kilopond metre per kilogram	kgf m/kg	9·806 65 J kg^{-1}
calorific value		kilocalorie per kilogram	kcal/kg	4·1868 kJ kg^{-1}
rate of heat flow		kilocalorie per second	kcal/s	4·1868 kW
heat capacity		kilocalorie per degree C	kcal/deg C	4·1868 kJ K^{-1}
entropy		kilocalorie per degree K	kcal/deg K	4·1868 kJ K^{-1}
specific entropy		kilocalorie per kilogram per °K	kcal/kg/°K	4186·8 J kg^{-1} K^{-1}
specific heat capacity		kilocalorie per kg per deg C	kcal/kg/deg C	4·1868 kJ kg^{-1} K^{-1}
thermal capacity per unit volume		kilocalorie per cubic metre per °C	kcal/m^3 deg C	4·1868 kJ m^3 K^{-1}
rate of heat dissipation		kilocalorie per square metre per second (surface)	kcal/m^2/s	4·1868 kW m^{-2}
rate of heat liberation (volume)		kilocalorie per cubic metre per second	kcal/m^3/s	4·1868 kW m^{-3}

physical quantity	symbol	metric technical unit	abbreviation	value in SI units
radiation co-efficient		kilocalorie per square metre per second K^4	kcal/m^2 s^{-1} K^4	4·1868 W m^{-2} K^4
thermal conductance		kilocalorie per square metre per second per °C	kcal/m^2 s	4·1868 W m^{-2} K
thermal conductivity		kilocalorie per metre per second per °C	kcal/m s deg C	4186·8 W m^{-1} K^{-1}
thermal re-sistivity		metre second deg C per kilocalorie	m s deg C/kcal	0·000 9 m K^{-1} W^{-1}

Conversion Table B3

SI and non-coherent metric units.

These are exact relationships except where marked *

physical quantity	symbol	metric technical unit	abbreviation	value in SI units
length	L	angström	Å	10^{-10} m
		international nautical mile	n mile	1852 m
		parsec	pc	$30·87 \times 10^{15}$ m
area	A	barn	b	10^{-28} m^2
		are	a	100 m^2
		decare	da	1000 m^2
		hectare	ha	10 000 m^2
volume	V	millilitre	ml	1·000 028 cm^3 *
		litre	l	1·000 028 dm^3 *
		hectolitre	hl	0·1 m^3 *
mass	m	gamma	γ	10^{-9} kg

physical quantity	symbol	metric technical unit	abbrev- iation	value in SI units
mass (ctd)		metric carat	CM	0·000 2 kg
		quintal	q	100 kg
		tonne (metric ton)	t	1000 kg
mass den- sity		kilogram per litre	kg/l	10^{-3} kg m^{-3} *
concentra- tion		gram per litre	g/l	1 kg m^{-3} *
		gram per millilitre	g/ml	999·972 kg m^{-3}
velocity	v	kilometre per hour	km/h	0·277 778 m s^{-1} *
		international knot	kn	463/900 m s^{-1}
		international knot	kn	0·514 444 m s^{-1}
acceleration	a	milligal	mgal	10^{-5} m s^{-2}
volume rate of flow		litre per hour	l/h	2·777 10^{-7} m^3 s^{-1} *
		litre per minute	l/min	1·666 10^{-6} m^3 s^{-1} *
		litre per second	l/s	1·000 028 × 10^{-3} m^3 s^{-1}
mass rate of flow		kilogram per hour	kg/h	2·777 78 kg s^{-1}
momentum	I	tonne metre per second	t m/s	1000 N s
angular momentum	L	tonne metre per second	t m/s	1000 N s
force	F	gram-force		0·009 806 65 N
		sthène	sn	1000 N
energy		electron volt	eV	1·602 10 × 10^{-19} J
		international joule (to 1948)		1·000 19 J
		calorie (thermochemical)		4·184 J
		calorie (15° C)	cal$_{15}$	4·1855 J
		calorie (international)	cal$_{IT}$	4·1868 J

physical quantity	*symbol*	*metric technical unit*	*abbreviation*	*value in SI units*
energy (ctd)		litre atmosphere	l atm	101·328 J
		kilowatt hour	kW h	3·6 MJ
		thermie	th	4·1855 MJ
		tonne calorie		4·1868 MJ
torque		gram-force centimetre	g cm	10^{-5} N m
power		torr litre per second	torr l/s	0·133 322 N m s^{-1}
		international watt (to 1948)		1·000 19 W
pressure		millitorr		0·133 322 N m^{-2}
		millibar	mb	100 N m^{-2}
		torr	mm Hg	133·3224 N m^{-2}
		pièze	pz	1000 N m^{-2}
		bar	bar	100 000 N m^{-2}
		hectopièze	hpz	100 000 N m^{-2}
		standard atmosphere	atm	101 325 N m^{-2}
		kilobar	kbar	100 MN m^{-2}
		megabar	Mbar	100 GN m^{-2}
rate of leak from vacuum systems		clusec		1·333 22 μN m s^{-1}
		lusec		133·322 μN m s^{-1}
		torr litre per second	torr l/s	0·133 322 N m s^{-1}
stiffness		gram-force per centimetre	g/cm	0·980 665 N m
kinematic viscosity	μ	metre squared per hour	m^2/hr	2·777 78 10^{-4}m^2 s^{-1}
calorific value (volume)		calorie per cubic centimetre	cal/cm^3	4·1868 MJ m^{-3}
		thermie per litre	th/l	4185·38 MJ m^{-3}

physical quantity	symbol	metric technical unit	abbreviation	value in SI units
specific energy		calorie per gram	cal/g	4·1868 kJ kg⁻¹
rate of heat flow		kilocalorie per hour	kcal/h	1·163 W
		calorie per second	cal/s	4·1868 W
heat capacity and entropy	S	calories per gram	cal/g	4·1868 J kg⁻³
specific entropy		calories per gram	cal/g	4·1868 J kg⁻³
specific heat capacity		calorie per litre per deg C	cal/l deg C⁻¹	4·1868 kJ m⁻³ K⁻¹
thermal capacity per unit volume		calorie per cubic cm per deg C	cal/cm³ deg C⁻¹	4·1868 MJ m⁻³ K⁻¹
rate of heat dissipation (surface)		kilocalorie per sq. metre per hour	kcal/m² h⁻¹	1·163 W m⁻² s⁻¹
		calorie per sq. cm	cal/cm²	41·868 kW m⁻²
rate of heat liberation (volume)		kilocalorie per cubic metre per hour	kcal/m³ h⁻¹	1·163 W m⁻³ s⁻¹
radiation coefficient		kilocalorie per sq. metre per hour° K⁴	kcal/m² h⁻¹ K⁻⁴	1·163 W m⁻² K⁻⁴
thermal conductance		kilocalorie per sq. metre per hour per deg C	kcal/m² h⁻¹ deg C⁻¹	1·163 W m⁻² K⁻¹
		calorie per sq. cm per second per deg C	cal/cm² s⁻¹ deg C⁻¹	41·868 W m⁻² K⁻¹
thermal conductivity		kilocalorie per metre per hour per deg C	kcal/m⁻¹ deg C⁻¹	1·163 W m⁻¹ K⁻¹

physical quantity	symbol	metric technical unit	abbreviation	value in SI units
specific energy		calorie per gram	cal/g	$4{\cdot}1868$ kJ kg^{-1}
rate of heat flow		kilocalorie per hour	kcal/h	$1{\cdot}163$ W
		calorie per second	cal/s	$4{\cdot}1868$ W
heat capacity and entropy	S	calories per gram	cal/g	$4{\cdot}1868$ J kg^{-3}
specific entropy		calories per gram	cal/g	$4{\cdot}1868$ J kg^{-3}
specific heat capacity		calorie per litre per deg C	cal/l deg C^{-1}	$4{\cdot}1868$ kJ m^{-3} K^{-1}
thermal capacity per unit volume		calorie per cubic cm per deg C	cal/cm^3 deg C^{-1}	$4{\cdot}1868$ MJ m^{-3} K^{-1}
rate of heat dissipation (surface)		kilocalorie per sq. metre per hour	kcal/m^2 h^{-1}	$1{\cdot}163$ W m^{-2} s^{-1}
		calorie per sq. cm	cal/cm^2	$41{\cdot}868$ kW m^{-2}
rate of heat liberation (volume)		kilocalorie per cubic metre per hour	kcal/m^3 h^{-1}	$1{\cdot}163$ W m^{-3} s^{-1}
radiation coefficient		kilocalorie per sq. metre per hour° K^4	kcal/m^2 h^{-1} K^{-4}	$1{\cdot}163$ W m^{-2} K^{-4}
thermal conductance		kilocalorie per sq. metre per hour per deg C	kcal/m^2 h^{-1} deg C^{-1}	$1{\cdot}163$ W m^{-2} K^{-1}
		calorie per sq. cm per second per deg C	cal/cm^2 s^{-1} deg C^{-1}	$41{\cdot}868$ W m^{-2} K^{-1}
thermal conductivity		kilocalorie per metre per hour per deg C	kcal/m^{-1} deg C^{-1}	$1{\cdot}163$ W m^{-1} K^{-1}

physical quantity	symbol	metric technical unit	abbrev-iation	value in SI units
		calorie per cm per second per deg C	cal/cm s deg C	418·68 W m^{-1} K^{-1}
thermal re-sistivity		cm second deg C per calorie	cm s deg C/cal	0·002 388 m K W^{-1}
		metre hour deg C per kilocalorie	m h deg c/kcal	0·859 845 m K W^{-1}
nuclear fuel irradia-tion		megawatt day per tonne	MW D/t	86·4 MJ kg^{-1}
radioactiv-ity		curie	Ci	37×10^9 s^{-1}
geomag-netic field		gamma	γ	10^{-9} T
dipole mo-ment		debye	D	3·335 64x10^{-30} C m
current	I	international ampere (to 1948)	A	0·999 85 A
potential difference	V	international volt (to 1948)	V	1·000 34 V
resistance	R	international ohm (to 1948)	Ω	1·000 49Ω
amount of substance		Normkibikmeter	Nm^3	$(22·4145)^{-1}$ kmol

Conversion Table B4

SI and British Units

Those marked * are exact relationships
** = symbol not available

physical quantity	symbol	British unit	abbreviation	value in SI units
length	L	mil (0·001")	'thou'	25·4 μm *
		iron (boot and shoe trade)	0·53 mm	
		inch	in	25·4 mm *
		link		0·201 168 m *
		foot	ft	0·3048 m *
		yard	yd	0·9144 m *
		fathom		1·8288 m *
		rod, pole or perch		5·0292 m *
		chain	surveyor's	20·1168 m *
		chain	engineer's	30·48 m *
		furlong		201·168 m *
		mile		1609·344 m *
		UK nautical mile		1853·184 m *
		telegraph nautical mile		1855·32 m *
area	A	square inch	in^2	645·16 mm^2 *
		square foot	ft^2	0·092 903 m^2
		square yard	yd^2	0·836 127 m^2
		square chain		404·686 m^2
		rood		1011·71 m^2
		acre		4046·86 m^2
		square mile		2·589 99 km^2
volume	V	cubic inch	in^3	16·387 1 cm^3

physical quantity	symbol	British unit	abbreviation	value in SI units
volume (ctd)		cubic inch	in^3	16·386 6 ml
		board foot (timber, see p339)		2·359 74 dm^3
		cubic foot	ft^3	0·028 316 8 m^3
		cubic foot	ft^3	28·316 1 litre
		cubic yard	yd^3	0·764 555 m^3
		cubic yard	yd^3	0·764 533 litre
		cord (timber)		3·624 56 m^3
		Petrograd standard (timber)	standard	4·672 28 m^3
		acre foot	acre ft	1233·48 m^3
capacity	V	minim	**	59·1939 mm^3
		minim	**	0·059 192 2 ml
		fluid drachm	**	3·551 63 cm^3
		fluid drachm	**	3·551 53 ml
		fluid ounce	fl oz	28·413 1 cm^3
		fluid ounce	fl oz	28·412 2 ml
		gill		0·142 065 dm^3
		gill		0·142 061 litre
		pint	pt	0·568 261 dm^3
		pint	pt	0·568 245 litre
		quart	qt	1·136 53 dm^3
		quart	qt	1·136 49 litre
		gallon	gal	4·546 092 dm^3
		gallon	gal	4·545 96 litre
		peck	pk	0·092 18 dm^3
		bushel	bu	36·368 7 dm^3
		chaldron		1·309 27 m^3
mass	m	grain (avoirdupois, Troy and apothecaries)	gr	64·798 91 mg *
		scruple		1·295 98 g

physical quantity	*symbol*	*British unit*	*abbreviation*	*value in SI units*
mass (ctd)		pennyweight	dwt	1·555 17 g
		dram (avoirdupois)	dr	1·771 85 g
		drachm (Troy or old apothecaries)		3·887 93 g
		ounce (avoirdupois)	oz du	28·349 g
		ounce (apothecaries)	oz apoth	31·103 5 g
		pound (avoirdupois)	lb	453·592 37 g *
		stone		6·350 29 kg
		quarter		12·700 6 kg
		slug		14·593 9 kg
		international wheat bushel (60 lb)		27·215 542 2 kg *
		cental (100 lb)	ctl	45·359 237 kg
		hundredweight	UK cwt	50·802 3 kg
		ton (long ton)	UK ton	1016·05 kg
		UK ton		1·016 05 tonne
mass per unit length		pound per yard	lb/yd	0·496 055 kg m^{-1}
		ton per mile	ton/mile	0·631 342 kg m^{-1}
		ton per 1000 yard	ton/1000 yd	1·111 16 kg m^{-1}
		ounce per inch	oz/in	1·116 12 kg m^{-1}
		pound per foot	lb/ft	1·488 16 kg m^{-1}
		pound per inch	lb/in	17·858 kg m^{-1}
mass per unit area		ton per square mile	ton/sq mile	0·000 392 298 kg m^{-2}
		pound per 1000 square feet	lb/1000 ft^2	0·004 882 43 kg m^{-2}
		hundredweight per acre	cwt/acre	0·012 553 kg m^{-2}

physical quantity	symbol	British unit	abbreviation	value in SI units
mass per unit area (ctd)		ounce per square yard	oz/yd^2	0·033 905 7 kg m^{-2}
		ton per acre	ton/acre	0·251 071 kg m^{-2}
		ounce per square foot	oz/ft^2	0·305 152 kg m^{-2}
		pound per square foot	lb/ft^2	4·882 43 kg m^{-2}
		pound per square inch	lb/in^2	703·070 kg m^{-2}
mass density		pound per cubic foot	lb/ft^3	16·018 5 kg m^{-3}
		pound per gallon	lb/gal	99·776 3 kg m^{-3}
		pound per gallon	lb/gal	99·779 2 g litre^{-1}
		slug per cubic foot	slug/ft^3	515·379 kg m^{-3}
		UK ton per cubic yard	ton/yd^3	1328·94 kg m^{-3}
		pound per cubic inch	lb/in^3	27·679 9 kg m^{-3}
specific volume	v	cubic foot per pound	ft^3/lb	0·062 428 m^3 kg^{-1}
concentration		grain per gallon	gr/gal	14·253 8 mg dm^{-3}
		grain per gallon	gr/gal	14·254 2 mg litre^{-1}
		ounce per gallon	oz/gal	6·236 02 kg m^{-3}
		ounce per gallon	oz/gal	6·236 19 × 10^{-3} kg litre^{-1}
		pound per gallon	lb/gal	99·776 kg m^{-3}
		pound per gallon	lb/gal	0·099 779 2 kg litre^{-1}
land drainage		cubic foot per 1000 acre	ft^3/1000 acre	0·006 997 m^3 km^{-2}
		cubic foot per 1000 acre	ft^3/1000 acre	6·997 litres km^{-2}

physical quantity	symbol	British unit	abbreviation	value in SI units
filtration		gallon per square yard per day	gal/yd² day⁻¹	$0.005\ 437\ \text{m}^3\ \text{m}^{-2}\ \text{day}^{-1}$
		gallon per square yard per day	gal/yd² day⁻¹	$0.000\ 063\ \text{mm s}^{-1}$
velocity	v	inch per minute	in/min	$0.423\ 33\ \text{mm s}^{-1}$
		foot per minute	ft/min	$0.005\ 08\ \text{m s}^{-1}$
		mile per hour	mile/h	$0.477\ 04\ \text{m s}^{-1}$
		mile per hour	mile/h	$1.609\ 344\ \text{km h}^{-1}$
		UK knot	UK kn	$0.514\ 773\ \text{m s}^{-1}$
		UK knot	UK kn	$1.853\ 184\ \text{km h}^{-1}$
volume rate of flow		gallon per hour		$1.262\ 8 \times 10^{-6}\ \text{m}^3\ \text{s}^{-1}$
		gallon per minute		$75.766\ 10^{-6}\ \text{m}^3\ \text{s}^{-1}$
		cubic foot per minute	ft³/min	$0.471\ 95\ \text{dm}^3\ \text{s}^{-1}$
		gallon per second	gal/s	$4.546\ 09\ \text{dm}^3\ \text{s}^{-1}$
		cubic foot per second	cusec	$28.3168\ \text{dm}^3\ \text{s}^{-1}$
		million gallon per day		$52.617\ \text{dm}^3\ \text{s}^{-1}$
mass rate of flow		pound per hour	lb/h	$0.125\ 998\ \text{g s}^{-1}$
		ton per hour	ton/h	$0.282\ 235\ \text{kg s}^{-1}$
		pound per second	lb/s	$0.453\ 592\ 37\ \text{kg s}^{-1}$
mass flow rate per unit		pound per hour per square foot	lb/h ft⁻²	$1.356\ 23\ \text{g m}^{-2}\ \text{s}$
momentum		pound foot per second	lb ft/s	$0.138\ 255\ \text{kg m s}^{-1}$
angular momentum		pound foot squared per second	lb ft²/s	$0.042\ 140\ 1\ \text{kg m}^2\ \text{s}^{-1}$
		slug foot squared per second	slug ft²/s	$1.355\ 82\ \text{kg m}^2\ \text{s}^{-1}$

physical quantity	symbol	British unit	abbreviation	value in SI units
acceleration	a	foot per second per second	ft/s^2	0·304 8 m s^{-2}
force	F	poundal	pdl	0·138 255 N
		ounce-force	ozf	0·278 014 N
		pound-force	lbf	4·448 22 N
		ton-force	tonf	9·964 02 kN
work and energy		foot poundal	ft pdl	0·042 140 1 N m
		foot pound-force	ft lbf	1·355 82 N m
		British thermal unit	Btu	1·055 06 kJ
		centigrade heat unit	Chu	1·900 4 kJ
		foot cubed atmosphere	ft^3 atm	2·869 2 kJ
		horsepower hour		2·684 52 MJ
		therm		105·506 MJ
torque	T	ounce force inch	ozf in	7061·55 μN m
		poundal foot	pdl ft	0·042 140 1 N m
		pound-force inch	lbf in	0·112 985 N m
		pound-force foot	lbf ft	1·355 82 N m
		ton-force foot	tonf ft	3·307 03 N m
power	P	foot pound-force per second	ft lbf/s	1·355 82 W
		horsepower	hp	745·700 W
		ton of refrigeration (Lloyds)		3938·87 kW
pressure and stress	p	poundal per square foot	pdl/ft^2	1·488 16 N m^{-2}
		pound-force per square foot	lbf/ft^2	47·8803 N m^{-2}
		inch of water	in H$_2$O	249·089 N m^{-2}
		foot of water	ft H$_2$O	2989·07 N m^{-2}
		inch of mercury	in Hg	3386·39 N m^{-2}

physical quantity	symbol	British unit	abbreviation	value in SI units
pressure and stress (ctd)		pound-force per square inch	lbf/in^2 (pai)	6894·76 N m^{-2}
		ton-force per square foot	tonf/ft^2	107·252 kN m^{-2}
		ton-force per square inch	tonf/in^2	15·4443 MN m^{-2}
section modulus	Z	inch cubed	in^3	1·638 71 × 10^{-5} m^3
second moment of area	I	inch to the fourth	in^4	0·416 231 × 10^{-6} m^4
		foot to the fourth	ft^4	0·008 630 97 m^4
stiffness and surface tension		pound-force per foot	lbf/ft	14·5939 N m^{-1}
		pound-force per inch	lbf/in	175·127 N m^{-1}
		ton-force per foot	tonf/ft	32·6903 kN m
moment of inertia	J	ounce inch squared	oz in^2	0·182 900 kg cm^2
		pound inch squared	lb in^2	2·926 40 kg cm^2
		pound foot squared	lb ft^2	0·042 1401 kg m^2
		slug foot squared	slug ft^2	1·355 816 kg m^2
dynamic viscosity		poundal second per square foot	pdl s/ft^2	1·488 16 N s m^{-2}
		pound-force second per square foot	lbf s/ft^2	47·8803 N s m^{-2}
		pound-force hour per square foot	lbf h/ft^2	172·369 kN s m^{-2}
kinematic viscosity	u	inch squared per hour	in^2/h	1·792 11 × 10^{-7} m^2 s^{-1}
		foot squared per hour	ft^2/h	2·580 64 × 10^{-5} m^2 s^{-1}

physical quantity	symbol	British unit	abbreviation	value in SI units
		inch squared per second	in²/s	6.4516×10^{-4} m² s⁻¹
		foot squared per second	ft²/s	$0.092\,903$ m² s⁻¹
calorific value (volume basis)		British thermal unit per cubic foot	Btu/ft²	37.2589 J m⁻³
		British thermal unit per gallon	Btu/gal	$0.232\,080$ kJ m⁻³
		British thermal unit per gallon	Btu/gal	$0.232\,08$ kJ litre⁻¹
		therm per gallon	therm/gal	23.2080 GJ m⁻³
specific energy	u	foot pound-force per pound	ft lbf/lb	$2.989\,067$ J kg⁻¹
calorific value		British thermal unit per pound	Btu/lb	2.326 J kg⁻¹
mass basis, specific latent heat		centigrade heat unit per pound	chu/lb	$4.186\,816$ kJ kg⁻¹
specific enthalpy		therm per ton	therm/ton	103.839 kJ kg⁻¹
rate of heat flow		British thermal unit per hour	Btu/h	$0.293\,071$ W
heat capacity	C	British thermal unit per deg F	Btu/°F	1899.11 J K⁻¹
and entropy	S	British thermal unit per °R	Btu/°R	1899.11 J K⁻¹
specific entropy		British thermal unit per pound °R	Btu/lb °R	4186.8 J kg⁻¹ K⁻¹
specific heat capacity		foot pound-force per deg F	ft lbf/lb°F	5.38 J kg⁻¹ K⁻¹
		British thermal unit per pound per deg F	Btu/lb°F	4.1868 kJ kg⁻¹ K

physical quantity	symbol	British unit	abbreviation	value in SI units
		centigrade heat unit per pound per deg C	Chu/lb °C^{-1}	4·1868 kJ kg^{-1} K^{-1}
thermal capacity per unit volume		British thermal unit per cubic foot per deg F	Btu/ft^3 °F^{-1}	67·0661 kJ m^{-3} K^{-1}
rate of heat dissipation (surface)		British thermal unit per square foot per hour	Btu/ft^2 h^{-1}	3·154 59 W m^{-2}
rate of heat liberation (volume)		British thermal unit per cubic foot per hour	Btu/ft^3 h^{-1}	10·3497 W m^{-3}
radiation coefficient		British thermal unit per square foot per hour per °R^4	Btu/ft^2 h^{-1} °R^{-4}	33·1156 W m^{-2} K^{-4}
thermal conductance	U	British thermal unit per square foot per hour per deg F	Btu/ft^2 h^{-1} deg °F^{-1}	5·678 26 W m^{-2} K^{-1}
thermal conductivity	λ or k	British thermal unit inch per square foot per hour per deg F	Btu in/ft^2 h^{-1} °F^{-1}	0·144 228 W m^{-1} K^{-1}
		British thermal unit foot per square foot per hour per deg F	Btu ft/ft^2 h^{-1} °F^{-1}	1·730 73 W m^{-1} K^{-1}
		British thermal unit inch per square foot per second per deg F	Btu in/ft^2 s^{-1} °F^{-1}	519·220 W m^{-1} K^{-1}
thermal resistivity		square foot hour deg F per Btu per foot	ft^2 h °F Btu^{-1} ft^{-1}	0·577 789 m K W^{-1}

physical quantity	symbol	British unit	abbrev-iation	value in SI units
		square foot hour deg F per Btu per inch	ft^2 h °F/Btu in^{-1}	6·933 47 m K W^{-1}
fuel con-sumption rating		mile per gallon	mile/gal	0·3540 km $litre^{-1}$
traffic fac-tors		ton mile		1635·17 kg km
		ton mile per gallon		0·3597 tonne km $litre^{-1}$
illumination		lumen per square foot (foot-candle)	lm/ft^2	10·7639 lux
luminance		foot-lambert	ft-lambert	3·426 26 cd m^{-2}
		candela per square foot	cd/ft^2	10·7639 cd m^{-2}
		candela per square inch	cd/in^2	1550·00 cd m^{-2}
electrical resistivity (formerly specific re-sistance)		ohm inch	Ωin	39·3701 ohm metre
current den-sity	J	ampere per square inch	A/in^2	1550·00 A m^{-2}
potential gradient	E	volt per inch	V/in	39·3701 V m^{-1}
		volt per mil	V/mil	39·3701 kV m^{-1}
magnetic flux density	B	maxwell per square inch	$maxwell/in^2$	1·55 10^{-5} T
magnetis-ing force	H	ampere (turn) per inch	A/in	39·3701 A m^{-1}

Conversion Table B5

SI and American units which differ from British units

Those marked * are exact relationships.

physical quantity	symbol (USA)	American unit	abbrev-iation	value in SI units
length	L	US survey foot		0·304 806 1 m
area	A	circular mil		506·707 μm²
capacity	V	fluid ounce	fl oz	0.029 57 dm³
		gill		0·118 294 dm³ 0·118 291 litre
		liquid pint		0·473 176 dm³ 0·473 163 litre
		dry pint		0·550 610 dm³ 0·550 595 litre
		liquid quart		0·946 352 dm³ 0·946 326 litre
		dry quart		1·101 221 dm³ 1·101 190 litres
		gallon	US gal	3·785 41 dm³ 3·785 31 litres
		peck		8·809 760 dm³ 8·809 120 litres
		bushel		35·2391 dm³ 35·2381 litres
		cranberry barrel		95·471 245 dm³ 95·468 332 litres
		dry barrel		115·627 378 dm³ 115·623 85 litres
		petroleum barrel		158·988 dm³ 158·982 litres
		acre foot (as used in irrigation)		1233·4829 m³ 1·233 445 × 10⁶ l
mass	M	dram (apothecary's)		3·887 93 g
		assay troy ounce	oz tr or	31·1035 g

physical quantity	*symbol (USA)*	*American unit*	*abbreviation*	*value in SI units*
mass (ctd)		troy pound	lb tr	373·242 g
		international corn bushel		27·215 542 2 kg *
		hundredweight	sh cwt	45·3592 kg
		ton (short ton)	sh ton	907·184 7 kg
concentration		pound per US gallon	lb/US gal	0·119 826 g cm^{-3} 0·119 830 g ml^{-1}
		grain per US gallon	gr/US gal	17·1181 g m^{-3} 17·1185 mg litre^{-1}
		ounce per US gallon	oz/US gal	7·489 15 g dm^{-3} 7·489 36 g litre^{-1}
force	F	ton-force	US tonf	8·896 44 kN
power		ton of refrigeration		3140·045 W

Conversion Table B6

Units of radiation

nature of unit	*obsolescent unit*	*SI unit*	*relationship*
activity	curie (Ci)	becquerel (Bq)	1 curie = 3·7 × 10^{10} Bq 1 Bq = 2·7 × 10^{-11} Ci
absorbed dose	roentgen (R) and rad (rd)	gray (Gy)	1 Gy = 100 rads
dose equivalent	rem	sievert (Sv)	1 Sv = 100 rems

Conversion Table B7

Units of pressure

current practice	value in the base SI unit $N\ m^{-2}$	SI
gaede	10^{-6}	µPa
	10^{-3}	mPa
barye or dyn/cm^2	0·1	
millitorr or micron Hg*	0·133	
	1	Pa
poundal/ft^2	1·49	
conventional mm H$_2$O or kgf/m^2	9·81	
lbf/ft^2	47·9	
	100	dPa
torr or conventional mm Hg*	133	
conventional inch H$_2$O	249	
pièze	1000	kPa
conventional foot H$_2$O	2990	
conventional inch Hg *	3386	
lbf/in^2 (psi)	6894	
technical atmosphere or kgf/cm^2	98×10^3	
bar	1×10^5	
standard atmosphere	$1·01 \times 10^5$	
	10^6	MPa
hectobar	10^7	
kilobar	10^8	
	10^9	GPa

* Hg is the abbreviation of *hydrogyrum*, the Latin word for mercury.

Appendix C

Units Outside the International System

(This list cannot, of course, be considered exhaustive)

The units of the two main systems outside SI are those of the c.g.s. system and of the imperial system. Both these sets of units have been dealt with in the text and in Appendix B. The following units are occasionally met with in newspaper and other reports, or are of historical interest.

angstrom: Symbol Å – an obsolescent unit of length used by physicists, equal to 10^{-10} m = 10^{-1} nm.

barn: a unit of cross-sectional area used by nuclear physicists. It is equal to 10^{-24} m^2 = 100 fm^2.

bulk barrel: (UK) 36 gallons of beer.

celo: once used for the unit of acceleration 1 ft/sec.

coal-equivalent: a unit of energy equal to that contained in a specified quantity of coal. The abbreviation MTCE means 'millions of tonnes coal equivalent'. Unit based on average value of the calorific value of coal. A crude value since different coals have different values of energy content. The term has been used extensively to compare national requirements from different sources of energy such as oil, tidal power, wind power, nuclear power etc.

cran: this unit has been used in the herring fishing industry over a period of more than 100 years. It has never been a unit of great precision. In 1852 it was fixed by Parliament at 37½ imperial gallons which seems to have averaged about 750 fish. Some reports have given the number as 1000 fish and others have given the weight as 4 cst avoirdupois.

dioptre: unit of refrative power of a lens equal to the reciprocal of the focal length in metres. Converging lenses are deemed to be of positive power; and diverging lenses, negative.

donum: unit of area in Cyprus equal to 1338 m^2 = 0·134 hectare: also called the scala.

dunum: unit of area in Israel, 1000 square metres.

feddan: Egyptian unit of land area equal to about 1 acre = 0·506 hectare.

fermi: a unit of length used by physicists, equal to 10^{-15} m, or one femtometre.

fillette: of champagne, a quarter standard bottle.

firkin: a former measure of capacity for beer and ale equal to one quarter of a barrel; still sometimes met with in connection with a small cask or tub for butter, lard etc. The beer barrel in recent years contained 36 imperial gallons.

fors: symbol f – name suggested by the SUB Committee in 1956 for the force represented by 1 gramme weight; 1 fors = g dynes.

funal: see sthene.

gee-pound: another name for the mass unit later called the slug (qv).

hogshead: of wine 63 wine gallons: of beer 52·5 imperial gallons.

hoppus foot: of wood, equal to 0·036 054 m^3

hundred: variations in the numerical value of this quantity still persist in a few places. In Tralee Bay, Irish Republic, there are 120 oysters to the hundred (1980s).

kip: kilo imperial pounds, that is 1000 lbs avoirdupois.

kit: of fish – 10 stone where 1 stone = 14 lbs avoirdupois. At Milford Haven the kit was only 8 stone.

magnum: of champagne, equivalent to two standard bottles.

merk: old Scottish unit of currency, originally worth about 2 guineas. The word merk was also used in Shetland to specify an area of land varying from ½ to 2 acres.

meshara: unit of land area in Iraq equal to 2500 m^2 or 0·62 acre.

mutchkin: liquid measure formerly used in Scotland equal to 4 gills = Scots pint of ½ choppin.

neper: symbol Np – used on the Continent to express ratio of two powers using a natural logarithm. Its relationship to the bel, which uses a logarithm to the base 10, is 1 neper = 8 8686 decibels.

noggin: this word has been used extensively in the north of England to denote of a pint of intoxicating liquor; with the ½ pint being called a gill. In the south of England the gill is a ¼ pint and this was the legal value.

nox: a unit of illumination suitable for very low levels such as moonlight. It is equal to 10^{-1} lux or 10^{-1} lumen/m.

pipe: a pipe of port wine is 2 hogsheads which is 126 wine gallons.

proof (percentage proof): a unit of strength of alcohol (ethanol). In former years tests to ascertain whether a distillate was 'over proof' or 'under proof' relied on whether or not gunpowder wetted by the liquid would or would not ignite after the alcohol itself had burned. Other tests included its burning qualities *per se*. An 'oil test' existed, relying on whether the liquid under test was denser or less dense than a certain oil. Subsequently hydrometers were employed. Proof spirit was defined in 1953 as an ethanol/water mixture of 12/13 the density of water at 50 degrees Fahrenheit. In the USA proof alcohol consisted of equal volumes of ethanol and water.

savart: unit of frequency ratios used in musical scales.

scala: see donum.

shekel: unit of money introduced in Israel on the 24th February 1980 to replace the former Israeli pound. The shekel was originally a measure of weight in gold or silver. It was first mentioned in the Book of Genesis, where Abraham paid to Ephron the Hittite '400 shekels of silver' for the Cave of Machpela in Hebron as a burial place for himself and his family. The shekel was then equal to about 11½ grams. It is now a purely monetary unit.

specific rotation [α] (optical rotation): a function of certain solids, liquids and solutions to rotate linearly polarized light. For solids the specific rotation is the optical rotation in degrees produced by 1 mm of solid. For solutes (substances in solution) $[\alpha] = 10^4 \, \alpha/dc$ where α is the observed rotation in degrees, d the length of the solution, and c the concentration in grams per 100 cm^3.

Rotations clockwise to an observer viewing against the direction of the light beam are deemed dextrorotatory and positive. Conversely, anticlockwise rotations are considered laevorotatory and negative.

spit: one garden spade's depth.

sthene: unit of force in the metre-tonne-second system of units, equal to 1000 newtons, also called the funal.

tank-pressure: a pressurised cabin is sometimes used for the treatment of patients suffering from multiple sclerosis. It is customary in the UK to rate the pressure (which is variable) in the terms of depth in feet in water. 1 foot of water = 0·434 lbs per square inch = 2992 pascals.

Troy ounce: the only part of the Troy system still in use. The price of gold is still quoted throughout the world in terms of its price per Troy ounce. 1 Troy ounce = 1·096 oz avoirdupois.

vergee: unit of land area in the Channel Islands.
In Jersey 1 vergee = 0·180 hectare = 0·445 acre.
In Guernsey 1 vergee = 0·162 hectare = 0·400 acre.

yard of ale: 2½ UK pints = 1·42 litres.

Arbitrary scales

Appendix D1

Beaufort Wind Force Scale

The Beaufort scale was originally devised by Francis Beaufort (1774–1857) in 1805. Initially based on the effect of the wind on a full-rigged man-of-war, by 1838 it became mandatory for log entries in all ships in the Royal Navy. The scale as used at sea was adopted (with additions and amendments) in 1874 by the International Meteorological Committee (IMC). Attempts to formulate a 'land' equivalent were made in 1912 and 1921; the latter by a G C Simpson whose proposals were accepted by the IMC in 1926. Other minor amendments were introduced in 1939 and 1955.

BEAUFORT SCALE *As used on land*

			wind-speed				descrip-
force	*descrip-tion*	*specifications for use on land*	*knots*		*kilometres hour^{-1}*		*tion in forecasts*
			mean	*range*	*mean*	*range*	
0	calm	calm; smoke rises vertically	<1	0–1	<1·5	0–1·5	calm
1	light air	direction of wind shown by smoke drift but not by wind vanes	2	1–3	3	1·5–5	light
2	light breeze	wind felt on face; leaves rustle; ordinary vane moved by wind	5	4–6	9	6–12	light

force	description	specifications for use on land	wind-speed				description in forecasts
			knots		kilometres hour^{-1}		
			mean	range	mean	range	
3	gentle breeze	leaves and small twigs in constant motion; wind extends light flag	9	7–10	16	13–19	light
4	moderate breeze	raises dust and loose paper; small branches are moved	13	11–16	25	20–30	moderate
5	fresh breeze	small trees in leaf begin to sway; crested wavelets form on inland waters	19	17–21	35	31–39	fresh
6	strong breeze	large branches in motion; whistling heard in telegraph wires; umbrellas used with difficulty	24	22–27	45	40–50	strong
7	near gale	whole trees in motion; inconvenience felt when walking against wind	30	28–33	56	51–61	strong
8	gale	breaks twigs off trees; generally impedes progress	37	34–40	68	62–74	gale

force	description	specifications for use on land	wind-speed				description in forecasts
			knots		kilometres hour^{-1}		
			mean	range	mean	range	
9	strong gale	slight structural damage occurs (chimney pots and slates removed)	44	41–47	81	75–87	severe gale
10	storm	seldom experienced inland; trees uprooted; considerable structural damage occurs	52	48–55	95	88–102	storm
11	violent storm	very rarely experienced; accompanied by widespread damage	60	56–63	109	103–116	violent storm
12	hurricane force	(no description)	-	>64	-	>117	hurricane

Chamber's Technical Dictionary, Eds Tweney and Hughes (1949) gives the following relationship between wind speed in miles per hour (V) and Beaufort scale numbers (B):

$$V = 1.87\sqrt{B^3}$$

Figures obtained using this formula are in good agreement with the mean wind-speeds listed in the table.

BEAUFORT SCALE, *As used as sea*

(for wind-speeds consult table as for use on land)

force	description	specifications for use at sea	description in forecasts	state of sea	typical height of waves in open sea – metres
0	calm	sea like a mirror	calm	calm	0·0
1	light air	ripples with the appearance of small wavelets	light	calm	0·1
2	light breeze	small wavelets still short but more pronounced; crests have a glassy appearance and do not break	light	smooth	0·2
3	gentle breeze	large wavelets; crests begin to break; foam of glassy appearance; perhaps scattered white horses	light	smooth	0·6
4	moderate breeze	small waves becoming longer; fairly frequent white horses	moderate	slight	1·0
5	fresh breeze	moderate waves, taking a more pronounced long form; many white horses are formed; chance of some spray	fresh	moderate	2·0

force	description	specifications for use at sea	description in forecasts	state of sea	typical height of waves in open sea – metres
6	strong breeze	large waves begin to form; the white foam crests are more extensive everywhere; probably some spray	strong	rough	3·0
7	near gale	sea heaps up and white foam from breaking waves begins to be blown in streaks along the direction of the wind	strong	very rough	4·0
8	gale	moderately high waves of greater length; edges of crests begin to break into spindrift; the foam is blown in well-marked streaks along the direction of the wind	gale	high	5·5
9	strong gale	high waves; dense streaks of foam along the direction of the wind; crests of waves begin to topple, tumble and roll over; spray may affect visibility	severe gale	very high	7·0

force	description	specifications for use at sea	description in forecasts	state of sea	typical height of waves in open sea – metres
10	storm	very high waves with long overhanging crests; the resulting foam in great patches is blown in dense white streaks along the direction of the wind; the 'tumbling' of the sea becomes heavy and shock-like; visibility affected	storm	very high	9·0
11	violent storm	exceptionally high waves; (small) and medium-sized ships might be for a time lost to view behind the waves; everywhere the edges of wave crests are blown into froth; visibility affected	violent storm	phenomenal	11·0
12	hurricane	the air is filled with foam and spray; sea completely white with driving spray; visibility very seriously affected	hurricane	phenomenal	14·0

Appendix D2

The Richter Scale

An intensity scale used to describe earthquake effects was devised in 1902 by the Italian seismologist Giuseppe Mercalli and updated in 1931 by American researchers. This 12-point scale (of Mercalli numbers) was of limited value in practice; it was based upon eye-witness accounts and hence was only qualitative in nature. Mercalli numbers are usually given in Roman numerals.

From 1935 onwards the Mercalli scale was superseded by the Richter scale in most countries. This scale is a quantitative one since it aims at specifying the order of magnitude of the energy released by the earthquake. (The scale is named after Charles Francis Richter.)

An instrument called the seismograph measures the vibrations of the earth resulting from an earthquake. The logarithm of the maximum amplitude of the deflection of the seismograph, measured in micrometres (μm), is used in the calculation of the Richter number. Since the various seimographs thoughout the world are situated at different distances from a given earthquake, allowance is made for the attenuation of the earth's vibrations and the value at 100 kilometres from the quake's epicentre is used in calculating the Richter number for which M is the usual symbol.

There are two empirical formulae relating the Richter number to the estimated value of the energy released. Using the symbol M for the Richter number and E for the energy released, the two formulae are as follows:

Gutenberg and Richter
$$\text{Log}_{10} \, E = 4{\cdot}8 + (1{\cdot}5 \times M) \quad \text{or} \quad E = 10^{(4{\cdot}8 + 1{\cdot}5\,M)} \text{ joules.}$$

Bäth

$\text{Log}_{10} \; E = 5 \cdot 24 + (1 \cdot 44 \times M)$ or $E = 10^{(5 \cdot 24 + 1 \cdot 44 \, M)}$ joules.

The increase in the value of the energy released from one Richter number to the next higher number is approximately as follows: according to Gutenberg 31 times, according to Bäth 27 times.

To envisage the enormous forces produced by the major earthquakes a comparison can be made between the energy released, usually in a few seconds, with the energy supplied to its consumers in a whole year by the Central Electricity Board. The unit of energy most familiar to the general public is that shown on his electricity bill. This is the kilowatt-hour which for convenience will be called in this context the Domestic Unit.

In the year 1986/87 the CEGB supplied to its consumers a total of $2 \cdot 284 \times 10^{11}$ Domestic Units = 228 400 000 000 Domestic Units.

The most severe earthquake recorded so far (1996) was that which occurred on 27 March 1964 at Prince William Sound, Alaska. This was of magnitude 8·8 on the Richter scale. Estimates of the energy released on this occasion are: Gutenburg $2 \cdot 8 \times 10^{11}$ kilowatt-hours, Bäth $2 \cdot 3 \times 10^{11}$ kilowatt-hours.

The Richter scale

estimated energy in kilowatt-hours (to 3 significant figures)

Richter number	Richter – Gutenberg	Bäth
1	0·6	1·3
2	18	36
3	554	1000
4	17 500	27 800
5	554 000	765 000
6	$1 \cdot 75 \times 10^{7}$	$2 \cdot 11 \times 10^{7}$
7	$5 \cdot 54 \times 10^{8}$	$5 \cdot 80 \times 10^{8}$
8	$1 \cdot 75 \times 10^{10}$	$1 \cdot 60 \times 10^{10}$
9	$5 \cdot 54 \times 10^{11}$	$4 \cdot 40 \times 10^{11}$
10	$1 \cdot 75 \times 10^{13}$	$1 \cdot 21 \times 10^{13}$

Appendix D3

Mohs' Scale of Hardness (of Minerals)

Mohs' scale is an empirical and arbitrary scale used to compare the relative hardness of minerals, not excluding semi-precious and precious stones. The scale, devised by Fredrich Mohs (1772–1839) in 1822, ordered ten reference minerals in a series from 1 to 10, talc being the softest and (hardly surprisingly) diamond the hardest. The values are not quantitative, but merely represent rank order of the materials. A stone of hardness 7 implies that the reference mineral 7, namely quartz, will neither scratch the stone, nor be scratched by it.

The following table lists the ten reference minerals.

Mohs' scale number	mineral	Mohs' scale number	mineral
1	talc	6	feldspar
2	gypsum	7	quartz
3	calcite	8	topaz
4	fluor	9	corundum
5	apatite	10	diamond

The scale is still employed widely. British Standard BS 6431 : Part 13 1986 *Method for determination of scratch hardness of surface according to Mohs* is employed in testing ceramic tiles.

An earlier 1 to 10 scale of hardness, for metals, had been devised by an Irish chemist Richard Kirwan (1733–1812). Tests included the following comparisons: against chalk (3), nail (4), knife (5, 6, 7); and the facility to strike no spark (8), feeble sparks (9), or lively sparks (10) against steel.[189]

Indentation hardness testing methods are due to Vickers, Rockwell, Brinell and Knoop. (See Kaye and Laby, 1995 ed).[144A]

Appendix D4

The Carat – fineness of gold and a mass unit

The carat – fineness of gold and jewellers' weight

There are two distinct meanings of the word carat. (In USA, karat.)

The first meaning and the most commonly met with is that in relation to gold. The number of carats denotes the number of 24th parts of the article which is pure gold. Thus an 18-carat wedding ring would contain 18/24 parts by weight of pure gold; this means ¾ of the total weight would be pure gold and ¼ base metal. In the United Kingdom it is illegal to describe an article as 'gold' if it is of fineness less than 9 carats, ie less than 3/8 pure gold by weight. There are four assay offices in the UK which are empowered to test articles for their gold content and impress upon the article a hallmark which gives the correct figure for the gold content.

In recent years another scale has been instituted giving the gold content in 'parts per thousand'. A crown mark followed by the figures '917', for example, indicates that the metal is at least 91·7 per cent pure gold.

The second meaning of the word carat is that relating to diamonds and other precious stones. The metric carat now in common use is, since 1 April 1914, equal to 1/5 of a gram or 200 milligrams. The agreed subdivision of the carat is the 'point', equal to 1/100 or 0·01 carat. The largest known diamond is the Cullinan, the uncut weight of which was 3106 carats or 621·2 grams, roughly 1½ lbs avoirdupois. This was cut into nine major diamonds and 96 minor diamonds. The largest of these weighs 530 carats and is on display in the Jewel House at the Tower of London. The second largest cut diamond weighs 407 carats and was sold in New York in 1988.

Appendix D5

Examples of dimensionless values

It is self-evident that dimensionless values do not possess units. But laboratory or field experiments that employed measurements are the basis of measurement (and hence determination) of these dimensionless attributes. The values obtained and recorded are subsequently relied on and used as reference values for other work.

Thus follows a few examples of some of the more common dimensionless sets that may be encountered.

relative density: the mass of a particular volume of a substance to the mass of an equal volume of water. For gases and vapours, the mass of a equal volume of hydrogen is employed.

relative humidity: the ratio of the pressure of the water vapour present to the saturation pressure of water at the same air temperature. It is usually expressed as a percentage.

refractive index: now defined as the reciprocal of the ratio of the speed of light (of a specified wavelength) in a medium (eg glass, water) to that in a specified reference medium (for precise work, free space; formerly air or a vacuum).
Note: Willebrord Snell in 1621 found that for any specific medium the ratio of the sine of the angle of incidence to the sine of the angle of refraction was a constant. This value came to be known as the refractive index. [Many materials, particularly crystalline substances, are noticeably birefringent eg magnesium fluoride, sapphire]

spectral emissivities: the ratio of energy radiated by an artifact to that radiated by a black body. See also page 274.

expansivity (thermal expansion): three members of this set; linear, superficial and volume:

respectively: α where $L_2 = L_1(1 + \alpha\theta)$
              β where $A_2 = A_1(1 + \beta\theta)$
              γ where $V_2 = V_1(1 + \gamma\theta)$

where a specimen increases from L_1 (or A_1, V_1) to L_2 (or A_2, V_2) when raised through $\theta°$ [assuming the relationship is not dependent on the temperature range considered].

partition coefficient: the ratio of the masses of a solute at equilibrium distributed between two immiscible solvents.

Poisson's ratio (v): the lateral contraction of a body per unit breadth divided by the longitudinal extension per unit length under an applied longitudinal stress. [examples: gold 0·44, lead 0·44, brass 0·35, aluminium 0·34, soft iron 0·29]

Appendix E

The United Kingdom's Monetary System

Prior to 1971

The smallest unit coin was the penny, denoted by the symbol d from the Latin *denarius*. A coin of half this value was in circulation and called the halfpenny (pronounced 'há-'penné' or 'há'pné'). Earlier on there had been a coin of only half the value of the halfpenny or quarter of a penny. This coin was called the 'farthing' ($\frac{1}{4}$d). In London this coin was in full circulation but was less well-known in some other parts of the United Kingdom. The farthing was withdrawn from circulation on 1 January 1960. From 1842 there was a coin of value one half-farthing or 1/8d; this was withdrawn in 1869.

Between 1860 and 1971, the penny and halfpenny were of weight designated that

3 pennies weighed one ounce avoirdupois

5 halfpennies weighed one ounce avoirdupois. (See Figure 35)

Incidentally, a halfpenny coin had a diameter of one inch.

From the lower unit of one penny was built up the system:

12 pence (12d) = 1 shilling, denoted s, from the Latin *solidus*.

20 shillings (20s) = 1 pound (sterling), symbol £, from the Latin *libra*.

The sixpenny coin was first struck in 1551, at the Tower Mint, in Southwark where Mint Street still exists, and also at York. Changes were made in the structure of this coin in 1662, 1674, 1816 and 1967.

Figure 35 – Britain's pre-decimal coins, in piles each weighing approximately one ounce avoirdupois.

Silver content of higher denomination coins

Before 1920, silver coins were struck in sterling silver, being 92·5% fine. These coins were the small threepenny-bit, the sixpence, shilling, two shilling piece, the half-crown, and the crown. A double-florin, value four shillings was issued in two years, (1887 & 1888), but proved unpopular owing to the ease with which it was confused with the crown coin. All these silver coins were of such weight that five shillings' face value weighed one ounce avoirdupois. (See Figure 35).

Sets of Maundy coins in denominations of 1, 2, 3, and 4 pence for limited distribution by the Monarch were struck in sterling silver until 1920, and again after 1947: that practice continues. In the intervening period, 50% fine alloy was used. Occasionally, commemorative crowns are struck in sterling silver; of interest to collectors.

Between 1920 and 1947 the silver coins minted for circulation contained 50% silver. But after World War II, Britain was obliged to repay to the USA 88 million ounces of silver, borrowed under a lease-lend agreement. So, by virtue of the Coinage Act 1946, newly minted 'silver' coins for circulation were struck in cupro-nickel (75% copper, 25% nickel), thus releasing silver for repayment to be made.

Decimal money after 15 February 1971 (then referred to as 'Decimal Day')

The new system of currency was required to be decimal in order to prepare for the metrication of weights and measures in the United Kingdom. Florins and double-florins had been minted much earlier in an abortive attempt to prepare for decimalisation. In the new 1971 system:

£1 = 100 new pence.

The agreed symbol for the new penny is p. Since in the former system £1 = 240d it followed that 1p = 2·4d, or 1 new penny = 2·4 old pennies. The designation 'new penny' was discontinued after about two years and the unit came to be known as 'penny'. See Figures 32 and 33 showing the first decimal coins and some of the attendant publicity (pages 294 and 295).

The redundant copper alloy coins – the 'old' penny and halfpenny and a twelve-sided threepenny piece (the latter coin introduced in 1937) – were, from decimal day, no longer legal tender. For a time some of the silver or cupro-nickel coins of the old system were retained in circulation, namely the shilling, equal to five new pence; and the two-shilling piece or florin, equal to ten new pence. It was difficult to fit into the new system the sixpenny coin, which became of value 2½p. The sixpence ceased to be legal tender after 30 June 1980.

From 1985 three new coins were introduced. These were a one pound coin, a seven-sided fifty-pence piece and a seven-sided twenty pence piece. From about 1987 and 1989 respectively, the original 5p and 10p denominations were replaced by less bulky coins of the same value. Commemorative £2 and £5 coins have been struck in a number of years in the 1990s.

It is intended that two new coins will be struck in 1997. These are a £2 bimetallic coin, composed of an inner disc of one alloy with a contrasting outer annular ring; and a fifty-pence piece, smaller than those that were initially introduced in 1985.

In December 1995 it was generally agreed by the EEC (the United Kingdom raising a dissenting voice) that a common European currency be introduced at about the end of 1999. It was decided to call the unit the euro.

Appendix F

pH values
(measures of acidity/alkalinity/neutrality)

The term and concept pH (pH: p, Potenz; H, Hydrogen [ions]) was introduced in 1909 by the Dane S P L Sørensen (1868–1939). No experimental methods exist to determine pH values with absolute accuracy as the *activity* of the hydrogen ions present rather than the *concentration* is the determinant. The pH value may be specified to a fairly high level of accuracy as follows: *the negative logarithm (to the base 10) of the concentration of hydrogen ions H^+ (aq) in mol dm^{-3} of solution.*

It will be appreciated that pH as so specified is a derived SI unit. Neutral or pure water is of pH7. Acidic aqueous liquids measure a lower pH; alkalis in aqueous solution have a higher pH, up to about pH 13–14.

Measurements of pH may be with pH meters (specially designed electronic meters), though satisfactory methods for less sophisticated work include the use of solutions of chemical indicators or broad or narrow range pH test papers impregnated with such chemical indicators. These papers remind one of litmus papers. In these latter two cases, the colour achieved in a test is compared with a graduated scale of colours, relevant to the indicator or mixture of indicators present. Table XXXI lists a few commonplace substances and their associated pH values. Table XXXII lists a few standard solutions of known pH.

Table XXXI
pH values of certain aqueous liquids

substance	pH value
car battery acid (20% w/v sulphuric acid)	< 1·0
stomach juices (containing hydrochloric acid)	1·6–1·9
orange juice (containing citric acid)	2·5–4·5
vinegar (about 5% ethanoic acid)	c 3·0
tomatoes/tomato juice	c 4·4
'acid rain' (sulphur dioxide/nitrogen oxides dissolved in the rain)	5·0–6·5
human saliva	6·3–6·9
cows' milk	6·6–6·9
human blood (naturally buffered)	7·3–7·5
human tears (naturally buffered)	7·4
egg white	8·0
sea water	8·0
household soap lather	c 10·0
sodium hydroxide solution (even a relatively dilute solution is strongly alkaline)	12–14

To adequately define the conditions for chemical tests and reactions (laboratory or industrial scale) particular pH levels must often be specified. Biochemical reactions too are frequently susceptible to the pH of the system.

Table XXXII
pH values of certain standard reference solutions (aqueous)

reference standard	pH at 20° C	pH at 30° C
0·1 mol kg^{-1} potassium tetroxalate	1·475	1·483
0·1 mol kg^{-1} potassium dihydrogen citrate	3·788	3·766
0·05 mol kg^{-1} potassium hydrogen phthalate	4·000	4·011
0·1 mol kg^{-1} disodium tetraborate	9·225	9·139
saturated calcium hydroxide	12·602	12·267

Appendix G

The Doppler effect and measurement of speed

Measurement of the speed of an object relative to an observer may be achieved by an application of a phenomenon identified in 1842 by Christian Johann Doppler (1803–1853), an Austrian physicist.

The Doppler effect allows astronomers to measure the speed of a luminous object such as a star relative to the observer. When the wavelengths of light emitted by a 'moving' star are measured, there is a shift in apparant wavelength which is a function of its speed. A star moving away from the earth *appears* to be emitting light of wavelengths longer than the actual wavelength, producing the so-called 'red shift'. Some distant galaxies are moving with such speed relative to observers on earth that the light emitted has shifted in apparant wavelength so far as to be outside the visible range.

Conversely to the 'red shift', a luminous object approaching the earth produces a 'blue shift' with light observed on earth to be of an apparently shorter wavelength.

Speeding motorists may be identified by devices that emit a 'radar' beam of electromagnetic radiation. Cameras incorporating a 24 GHz radio beam transmitter have been in common use in Britain since 1994. This beam is reflected from the vehicle body, the rebounding rays having the same wavelength only if the object is stationary. A car approaching the speed camera or radar gun reflects a beam, that 'shifts' to a shorter wavelength to that of the stationary reflector. In a converse manner, a vehicle travelling away from a speed detector causes a 'red shift'. In either case the speed of the vehicle may be calculated.

Appendix H

Dimensional analysis

Dimensional analysis is a useful tool in the field of measurements. It can often assist a human operator when he or she is handling an equation or attempting a solution to a problem by analysing the dimensions in which the function is expressed.

The dimensions of the units of a physical quantity are the powers to which the "fundamental" units (mass, length and time) are raised to describe that physical quantity. Other attributes could, of course, have been selected and designated "fundamental".

The essentials of dimensional analysis may be expressed by the following aphorisms:

The dimensions in each of two sides of a (correct) equation must be reconcilable.

If two sides of an equation do not have the same or the correct dimensions, then the equation is wrong.

If the dimensions of the solution to an equation or problem are known, then the function that will solve the equation must simplify to produce an answer with those dimensions.

An equation with consistent dimensions may still be wrong. However the error may be more likely to be in the arithmetic than the method of solution.

Table XXXIII

Dimensional formulae of common units

unit	dimension	dimensional formula
mass	("fundamental")	M
length	("fundamental")	L
time	("fundamental")	T
velocity	distance/time	LT^{-1}
acceleration	velocity/time	LT^{-2}
force	mass × acceleration	MLT^{-2}
momentum	mass × velocity	MLT^{-1}
energy	force × distance	$ML^2\,T^{-2}$
moment of inertia	mass × radius^2	ML^2
area	length^2	L^2
volume	length^3	L^3
pressure	force/area	$ML^{-1}\,T^{-2}$

Checking equations – some simple illustrations

(i) The area of an ellipse A is given by πab (ie $\pi \times a \times b$), where π is a dimensionless constant, and a is the major axis and b is the minor axis of the ellipse.

area $[L^2] = \pi \times a[L] \times b[L]$. Both sides of the equation are reconcilable.

(ii) A piston in a cylinder of diameter 0·5 metre is subject to a fluid pressure of 20 kilopascals. The force on the piston due to the liquid is given by:

force $[MLT^{-2}]$ = pressure $[ML^{-1}\,T^{-2}] \times$ area $[L^2]$. Both sides reconcile.

(iii) If g (an acceleration) is known to be related to the length of a pendulum L and the period of oscillation T^{-1}, then the only way that g can be related to the two variables L and T^{-1} is as follows:

g $[LT^{-2}]$ = (dimensionless constant) $\times L \times T^{-1} \times T^{-1}$

Appendix J

Disciplines, techniques of measuring and limitations resultant on measurements

Disciplines of human activity

As readers will appreciate, there are innumerable different disciplines, each with its own demands for measurements to be made. It is clearly beyond the scope of these two volumes to cover or review either the full range of these measurements; or the wide range of instruments, apparatus or associated procedures. Clearly readers must study the literature and other sources of data relevant to their fields of interest.

Among the most detailed collection of specifications of items and measuring techniques is that of the British Standards Institution. The catalogue, more bulky than a telephone directory, lists thousands of descriptions of specifications that are available from a wide range disciplines.

Measuring instruments

Other matters that any practitioner should bear in mind are that collection of data involving any measurements, apart from those involving small integers, are only samples from a population of an infinite set. See below for a brief comment on sampling. Errors, small or large, by the very nature of collecting data of continuous variables are bound to occur. One could measure a phenomenon, article or event, *ad infinitum*, and never obtain an *exactly* correct value. Almost all measurements are approximations.

Nor should anyone place undue reliance on any measuring instrument. The Editor recalls a Station Routine Order seen during his RAF National Service in 1954, ordering the recall of certain steel rules as they were short by a small fraction of an inch. It should be borne in mind that instruments may have been damaged, internal batteries low, or any pre-setting incorrect. The operator may not know how to use them. In use, instruments inevitably tend to become less accurate, and eventually wear out. A counsel of eternal caution is advised.

From the 1970s many instruments; eg micrometers, pH meters, electrical multimeters and pyrometers; were constructed, not with analogue scales, but with digital displays. Initially these were constructed with light-emitting diodes (LEDs) but by 1980 these gave way to liquid-crystal displays (LCDs). Whilst such instruments are probably more accurate, nonetheless the values displayed are still subject to error.

An interesting journal, *Weighing and Measuring* (Lincoln Publishing) reported on "international developments in industrial, commercial, laboratory and domestic weighing, measuring, metrology and transducer technology". Founded in 1983, it ceased publication in 1992.[191]

Observer skill

Observations are likely to reflect the skills and experience of the observer. Analogue readings may be unreliable if the practitioner does not know that parallax errors must be avoided. There may be lack of familiarity with the instrument, or the observer may confuse a scale on a new instrument with the *apparantly* similar but different scale on a former familiar dial.

Some terms met in relation to measurement practice

Accuracy refers to the closeness of measurements to the true value.

Precision describes the closeness of replicates of a measurement to each other.

When an operator uses the same apparatus, his results are a measure of **repeatability**. Results by different operators using different apparatus reflect **reproducibility**.

Sampling may be defined as the collection of a sub-set of items or observed phenomena from a **population** set. The **sample** may be a **random sample** or a **systematically collected sample**, or it may be a **biased** (and possibly unrepresentative).

Sampling theory and practice are disciplines in themselves: some knowledge about them can only be a useful guide for all practitioners of measurement. For example, the *Weights and Measures Act 1979* imposed certain duties of sampling and weighing on suppliers of goods – see Figure 36.

If readers wish to involve themselves in a fuller consideration of measuring techniques, and how to reconcile practice with perfection, they are advised to consult some books on elementary statistics. Some grasp of the 'essentials' of statistics is sure to be illuminating for any person who wishes to place more considered reliance on measurements that he or others have made or intend to make.

c. 45   1097

Weights and Measures Act 1979

1979 CHAPTER 45

An Act to make further provision with respect to weights and measures.   [4th April 1979]

BE IT ENACTED by the Queen's most Excellent Majesty, by and with the advice and consent of the Lords Spiritual and Temporal, and Commons, in this present Parliament assembled, and by the authority of the same, as follows:—

PART I

PACKAGED GOODS

Quantity control

1.—(1) It shall be the duty of a person who is the packer or importer of relevant packages to ensure that when a group of the packages marked with the same nominal quantity is selected in the prescribed manner and the packages in the group or such a portion of the group as is so selected are tested in the prescribed manner by an inspector— *Duties of packers and importers of packages.*

    (a) the total quantity of the goods shown by the test to be included in the packages tested divided by the number of those packages is not less than the nominal quantity on those packages ; and

    (b) the number of non-standard packages among those tested is not greater than the number prescribed as acceptable in relation to the number tested.

(2) Regulations in pursuance of the preceding subsection with respect to the manner of selecting or testing packages may, without prejudice to the generality of the powers to make regulations conferred by that subsection or to the generality of section

Figure 36 – Title page of Weights and Measures Act 1979.

References and Further Reading

Volumes 1 & 2

Most of these works are cited in the two volumes of *The Basis of Measurement*. However, the list also includes items that support the texts, and thus enable the readers to follow further their areas of special interest.

1   Jerrard, H G and McNeill, D B (5th edition 1986) *A Dictionary of Scientific Units including Dimensionless Numbers and Scales*: Chapman and Hall.

2   Iversen, Erik (1955) *Canon and Proportions in Egyptian Art*: Sidgwick & Jackson, London, Copenhagen [printed].

3   Hanke, R (1959) Beiträge zum Canonproblem, *Zeitschrift für Ägyptische Sprache und Altertumskunde* 84, pp113–119.

4   Vitruvius Pollio, Marcus (27 BC-AD 14) *De Architectura* [dedicated to Emperor Augustus].

5   Granger, Frank (2nd edition 1955) *Translation of De Architectura* [Ref 4, in two volumes]: The Loeb Classical Library.

6   Lorenzen, E (1966) *Technological Studies in Ancient Metrology*: Copenhagen [printed].

7   Gibson, Charles and Bonomi, Joseph (3rd edition 1872) *Proportions of the Human Figure*: Charles Robertson, London.

8   Michaelis, A D (1833) Ancient Marbles of Great Britain, *Journal of Hellenic Studies*: London.

9   Berriman, A E (1964) *Historical Metrology. A New Analysis of the Archaeological and Historical Evidence Relating to Weights and Measures*: Dent.

10   Skinner, F G (1967) *Weights and Measures*: HMSO. [Withdrawn from publication].

11 Kisch, Bruno (1965) *Scales and Weights. A Historical Outline, Yale studies in the History of Science No 1*: Yale University Press.

12 Prior, Miss W H (1924) Notes on the Weights and Measures of Medieval England, *Bulletin du Cange*: Edward Champion, Paris.

13 Hooper, G (1721) *An Inquiry into the State of the Ancient Measures, the Attick, Roman, and especially the Jewish*: R Knaplock, London.

14 Greaves, John (2nd edition 1745) *The Origin and Antiquity of our English Weights and Measures discovered by the near Agreement with such standards that are now found in one of the Egyptian Pyramids*.

15 Cumberland, Richard (2nd edition 1699) *An Essay Towards the Recovery of the Jewish Measures and Weights*: Richard Chivell, London.

16 Harkness, William (1888) The Progress of Science as Exemplified in the Art of Weighing and Measuring, *Bulletin of the Philosophical Society of Washington*: Annual address of the President.

16A Alexander, Pat. Organising editor, et al (Revised edition 1986) *The Lion Encyclopedia of the Bible*: Lion Publishing.

16B Jones, Alexander General Editor (Revised edition 1985) *The New Jerusalem Bible*: Darton, Longman and Todd.

16C (1962) *The Interpreter's Dictionary of the Bible Vol 4*, Weights and Measures p828: Abingdon Press, New York.

16D (1973) *Ecumenical Edition of the Revised Standard Version of the Bible*: Collins.

16E (1986) *Colliers Encyclopedia Vol 23*, Weights and Measures p387: Macmillan Educational Company.

17 Miskimin, Harry A (2nd series 1967) Two Reforms of Charlemagne, Weights and Measures in the Middle Ages, *The Economic History Review Vol XX*.

18 Leake, Stephen Martin (3rd edition 1793) *An Historical Account of English Money*: London.

19 Gras, Norman Scott Brien (1918) *Early English Custom System*: Harvard University Press.

20 Lipson, Ephraim (11th edition 1956) *Economic History of England. Vol 1 The Middle Ages*: Black.

21 Robertson, Agnes Jane (editor) (1925) *The Laws of the Kings of England from Edmund to Henry 1st*: Cambridge University Press.

22 Harmer, F E (Ed) (1914) *Select English Historical Documents of the Ninth and Tenth Century*: Cambridge University Press.

23 Hart, Cyril (1977) Two Queens of England, *Ampleforth Journal LXXXII Part II*.

24   Anon (c1500) *A Relation or rather a true Account. Island of England about the year 1500. By a Visitor to England*: Camden No 371847.

25   Chadwick, H Munro (1905) *Studies on Anglo-Saxon Institutes*: Cambridge University Press.

26   Luard, H R (Ed) (1859) *Bartholomaei de Cotton Historia Anglicana* AD 449–1298: Rolls Series.

27   Browne, W A (8th edition 1899) The Money, Weights and Measures of the Chief Commercial Nations of the World: Edward Stanford.

28   Worlidge, John (1704 and 1717) Dictionarium Rusticum et Urbanicum.

29   Jeake, Samuel (1701, 1st edition 1674) A compleat body of arithmetic . . . : London.

30   Salzmann, Louis Francis (1964, 1st edition 1931) English Industries in the Middle Ages: Oxford University Press.

31   Bailey, Natham (30th edition 1802, 1st edition 1721) The Universal Etymological English Dictionary: Glasgow. [Reprinted by various booksellers].

32   Harris, John (5th edition 1736, 1st edition 1704) Lexicon Technicum Or An Universal English Dictionary of Arts and Sciences . . .: London.

33   Kingdon, J A (1886) Introduction to: Archive of the Company of Grocers of the City of London, first vol of 175, [Facsimile].

34   Ruding, Roger (1817–19) Annals of the Coinage of Britain . . .: Nichols Son & Bentley, London.

35   Hearne, Thomas (Ed) (1775) A Collection of Curious Discourses written by Eminent Antiquaries, (two volumes): W & J Richardson, London.

36   Agarde, Arthure (not dated – c1610 –1660) An Essay.

37   Oman, Charles W C (8th edition 1938) A History of England, Volume 1, England before the Norman Conquest: Methuen & Co, London.

38   Attenborough, F L (1922) The Laws of the Earliest English Kings: Cambridge University Press.

39   Alexander, John Henry (1850) Universal Dictionary of Weights and Measures . . .: William Minifie & Co, Baltimore.

40   Barlow, Frank (several editions 1955–1972) The Feudal Kingdom of England 1042–1216: Longmans.

41   (3rd series, Vol 69 1859) The Kalendar of Abbot Samson of Bury St Edmunds and related documents: Camden Society.

42   *The Domesday of St Pauls in the year 1222* (cited in Ref 43).

43   Hale W H *Introduction to Ref 42.*

44 (Vol 2 1728) *Chambers Cyclopedia or An Universal Dictionary of Arts and Sciences.*

45 Oman, Charles (1931) *The Coinage of England*: Oxford University Press.

46 Cay, J (1739, 1758, 1766) *Cay's editions of public statutes.* [continued/edited by H B Cay].

47 Anon, (An unknown author in the Fleet Prison) (c1290) *Fleta.*

48 Nichols, F M (1955) *Fleta: [Introduction to translation of Reference 47] Volume 72*: Seldon Society.

49 Richardson, M G and Sayles, G O (1955) *Fleta [Translation of Reference 47] Volume 72*: Seldon Society.

50 Zupko, Ronald Edward (1968) *A Dictionary of English Weights and Measures from Anglo Saxon Times to the Nineteenth Century*: University of Wisconsin Press.

51 Power, Eileen and Postan, M M (1966) *Studies in English Trade in the Fifteenth Century*: Routledge & Kegan.

52 *An Account of the Proceedings and Report of a Committee of the House of Commons Appointed in 1758 to Enquire into The Original Standards of Weights and Measures in this Kingdom, and to Consider the Laws Relative Thereto.*

53 Hibbert, William N (1925) *History of the Worshipful Company of Founders of the City of London*: London, Livery Companies.

54 Hall, Hubert and Nicholas J Frieda (Eds) (Lloyd, J of Denbyshire) (c1603–1625) *A dissertation addressed to James 1st.*

55 Chaney, H James (1987) *Our Weights and Measures*: Eyre and Spottiswoode.

56 *Statutes of the Realm*, printed for the British Museum Library (now the British Library).

57 Riley, Henry Thomas (Ed) (1868) *Memorials of London and London Life, a series of Extracts . . . 1371*: London.

58 Powell, John (revised by) (1600) *The Assize of Bread.*

59 W P (translator, from Dutch) (1596) *The Pathway to Knowledge.*

60 Maitland, Frederic William (1907) *Domesday Book and Beyond*: Collins.

61 Arnold, R (republished 1811?) *The Customs of London, otherwise called Arnold's Chronicle* (not an original composition; copied from other sources.) [Richard Arnold is thought to have lived from 1450 to 1521. Original manuscript lost.].

62 Allen, Thomas (1828) *The History and Antiquities of London, Vol 3, Westminster, Southwark and parts adjacent*: Cowie and Strange.

63   Lane, Peter (Vol 1 1750–1870; 1973; Vol 2 1870–1939; 1975) *Documents of British Economic and Social History*: Macmillan.

64   (c1200) *The Record of Caernarvon*.

65   Record(e), Robert (1543) *The groüd of Artes Teachyng the worke and practice of Arithmetike . . .:* R Wolfe, London.

66   Sapwell, John (1960) *A History of Aylsham*: The Rigby Printing Co Ltd, Norwich.

67   Power, E (translator) (1937) Boissonnade, P; *Life and Work in Mediaeval Europe*: Kegan Paul Trench Trubner.

68   Rogers, Thorold, Quoted in Ref 134, p546.

69   Seebohm, Frederic (1914) *Customary Acres and Their Historical Importance*: Longmans Green.

70   Roberts, James (3rd edition 1908) *Weights and Measures*: Charles Knight, London.

70A Percival, John (1921) *The Wheat Plant*: Duckworth, London.

70B Beaven, E S (1947) *Barley, Fifty Years of Observation and Experiment*: Duckworth, London.

70C Darwin, Charles (1905 edition) *The Variations of Animals and Plants under Domestication*: John Murray.

71   Chisholm, H W (1877) *On the Science of Weighing and Measuring and Standards of Measure and Weight*: Macmillan.

72   (1932) *Register of Edward The Black Prince The Palatinate of Chester* AD 1351–1365: preserved in the Public Record Office, HMSO.

73   Tanner, J R (Ed) (1971) Tudor Constitutional Documents AD 1485–1603: Cedric Chivers.

74   Richardson, M G and G O Sayles (1935) Rotuli Parliamentorum, Third Series, Vol 51: Camden Society.

75   Luard, H R (Ed) (1858) Rerum Britannicarum medii aevi Scriptores: Cambridge.

76   Riley, H T (translator) (1861) Carpenter, John (Common Clerk) and Whittington, Richard (Mayor of London) (1419) Liber Albus. The White Book of the City of London.

77   Dalton, Michael (5th editon 1635) The Countrey Justice.

78   Wilde, Edith E (1931) Weights and Measures of The City of Winchester: Hampshire Field Club.

79   Cotton, Sir Robert (Ed) (1657) An Exact Abridgment of the Records in the Tower of London.

80 Evans, John (1966) The Flowering of the Middles Ages: Thames and Hudson.

81 Hylles, Thomas (1600) The arte of vulgar arithmeticke: G Simson

82 (1969) Rules for the Weighing and Taxation of English Cloth in Venice 1440, English Historical Documents Vol IV, P1038: Eyre and Spottiswoode.

83 Ridgeway, William (1892) The Origin of Metallic Currency and Weight Standards: Cambridge University Press.

84 Colyn, John (1517) The Commonplace book of John Colyn a London Mercer.

85 Connor, Prof R D (1987) The Weights and Measures of England: HMSO.

86 Hopton, Arthur (1635) Hopton's Concordancy Enlarged, of Weights and Measures used in England: London [Author not to be confused with contemporary, Sir Arthur Hopton].

87 Citizen, H G (1603) The Gouldsmythes Storehouse.

88 Swinton, John (Lord) (1779) *A Proposal for Uniformity of Weights and Measures in Scotland*: Edinburgh.

89 Nicholson, Edward (1912) *Men and Measures*: Smith, Elder and Co.

90 (1969) *English Historical Documents, Vol IV* p1084: Eyre and Spottiswoode.

91 Benese, Sir Rycharde de (c1540) Thomas Colwell's edition 1562/63 *This boke sheweth the maner of measuring*.

92 (First printed 1543, last edition 1714) *Assize of Bread*.

93 Langland, William (1978) *Piers Plowman, Translation of C-text (1398/99) by Derek Pearsal*: York Medieval Texts: 2nd Series, Vol VI, line 224, Edward Arnold

94 Pemberton, H (1746) *Translation and Improvement of the London Dispensatory*: Royal College of Physicians, London.

95 Macpherson, David (1805) *Annals of Commerce, Fisheries and Navigation . . .*: London.

96 (1820) *Second Report of the Commissioners Appointed by His Majesty to Consider the Subject of Weights and Measures, (Vol 7)*: Report from Commissioners, p1–40.

97 Alexander, John Henry (1857) *An Inquiry into the English System of Weights and Measures*: J H and J Parker, Oxford.

98 Jewell, Brian (1978) *Veteran Scales and Balances*: Midas Books.

99 Miskimin, H A (1970, 14th edition) in *Encyclopaedia Britannica* Vol 18, p39.

100   Peterson, H B A (1969) *Anglo Saxon Currency King Edquis Reform to the Norman Conquest*: Spink and Sons.

101   (1966) *Chambers Encyclopaedia.*

102   (1873) *Warden of the Standards 7th Annual Report*: HMSO.

103   Digges, Leonard (1st edition 1556, 1614 edition) *A Booke named Tectonicum . . .*

104   Alexander, John Henry (1850) *Universal Dictionary of Weights and Measures Ancient and Modern*: Wm Minifie & Co, Baltimore.

105   Challis, C E (2nd series 1967) The Debasement of The Coinage 1542–1551, *The Economic History Review, Vol XX.*

106   Kelly, Patrick (1816) Metrology or an Exposition of Weights and Measures, chiefly those of Great Britain and France, *The British Review*: No XXVI.

107   Kelly, Patrick (1817) Dissertation on Weights and Measures and the best means of revising them, *The British Review*: No XXVII.

108   Porter, Charles (1970 14th edition) *Encyclopaedia Britannica*, Vol 18 Lewin, p391.

109   Riley, Henry Thomas (1859) *Munimenta Gildhallae Londoniensis*: 'Chronicles and Memorials' Series.

110   (1884) *The Great Roll of the Pipe for the Fifth Year of the Reign of King Henry II* AD 1158–1159: The Pipe Roll Society Publications.

111   Reynardson, Samuel (1750) A State of the English Weights and Measures of Capacity . . .: London.

112   Asimov, Isaac (Ed) (1961) Asimov's Encyclopaedia of Science and Technology: George Allen and Unwin.

113   Hall, Hubert (Ed) (two vols 1912, 1914) Report of the Royal Commission on Public Records.

114   Granger, Allan (1917) Our Weights and Measures: Eyre and Spottiswoode.

115   Ellis, B (1966) Basic Concepts of Measurement: Cambridge University Press.

116   Hawkins, William Sergent (Ed) (1735) An Ordinance of Measures the 31st of Edward 1st AD 1302.

117   (1908) Annual Report of The British Weights and Measures Association.

118   Powicke, F Maurice (1953) The Thirteenth Century, 1216–1307: Clarendon Press, Oxford

119   Thompson, W S (Ed) (1944) A Lincolnshire Assize Roll for 1298; Vol 36: Lincoln Rec Soc.

120   Luard, H S (Ed) (1866) The Affairs of Dunstable Priory 1272–95, Annales Morsici: III Rolls Series.

121   Hallock, W and Wade, H T (1906) Outlines of the Evolution of Weights and Measures and the Metric System: Macmillan, New York.

122   Petrie, W M Flinders in (1888 9th edition) Encyclopaedia Britannica, Vol 24, Weights and Measures: Adam & Charles Black, Edinburgh.

123   Barnard (1879) The Metric System: Boston, USA.

124   Keith, George Skene (1817) Different Methods of establishing an Uniformity of Weights and Measures stated and compared: London, Aberdeen [Printed].

125   Pordes, H (1923) English Industries of the Middle Ages, [not in British Museum catalogue].

126   Robinson, E and McKie, D (Eds) (1970) Partners in Science, Letter of James Watt and Joseph Black: Harvard University Press.

127   (1963) Speculum vol XXXVIII.

128   Watson, Andrew M (2nd series 1967) Back to Gold and Silver, The Economic History Review, Vol XX No 1.

129   Grueber, Herbert A (1899) A Handbook of the Coins of Great Britain and Ireland in the British Museum: British Museum, London.

129A Grueber, Herbert A (1899) Kent, J P C et al (Eds) (1970) A Handbook of the Coins of Great Britain and Ireland in the British Museum: Spink & Son, London. [Revision of Reference 129]

130   Nolan, Dom Patrick (1926/28) A Monetary History of Ireland: P & S King & Sons, Bruges [Printed].

131   Kelly, Patrick (2nd edition, Vol 1 1835) *The Universal Cambist*: Longman.

132   Warburton, Rev W P (1924) *Edward III*: Oxford.

133   Anon, probably Samuel Reynardson.

134   Cunningham. W (4th edition, 1905) *The Growth of English Industry and Commerce during the Early and Middle Ages, Vol 1*: Cambridge University Press.

135   Barrow, G W S (Ed) (1960) *Regesto regum Scottorum, The Acts of Malcolm IV, King of Scots 1153–1165*: Edinburgh University Press.

136   Seebohm, Frederic, quoted in Ref 134, p327.

137   Cunningham, W (5th edition 1910) *The Growth of English Industry and Commerce during the Early and Middle Ages*: Frank Cass & Co Ltd.

138   Feavearyear, Albert E; Morgan E Victor (revised) (2nd edition 1963) *The Pound Sterling, A History of English Money*: Clarendon Press, Oxford.

139   Sheppard, T and Musham, J F (1923) *Money, Scales and Weights*: Spink
       and Son.

140   Hall, Hubert and Nicholas, Frieda J (Eds) (1929) *Select Tracts and Table
       Books Relating to English Weights and Measures 1188–1742*: 3rd Series
       Camden Society.

141   Harris, Preston (Ed) (1929) *Camden Miscellany XV, Vol XLI*: 3rd Series
       Camden Society.

142   Postlethwayt, Machaly (4th edition 1774) *The Universal Dictionary of
       Trade and Commerce, Vol II*: London.

143   Prior, W H (Ed) (c1925) *Acts of the Parliament of Scotland*: Cambridge.

144   Trevelyan, G M (1952) *Illustrated English Social History, Vol 1*:
       Longmans Green.

144A   Kaye, G & A and Laby, T H (1911) *Physical and Chemical Constants*:
       Longmans Green [this edition gives the 'mercury column' definition of the
       ohm].

144B   Eden, P (1995) Scientists with a degree of skulduggery, *Sunday Telegraph*
       January 22, 1995 p30.

145   Hoover, H C and Hoover, L H (translators) (1912) Agricola, Georgius
       (1556) De Re Metallica, *The Mining Magazine*.

146   Fleetwood, Bishop William (1707) *Chronicon Preciosum; or An Account
       of English Money, etc*: London [later edition includes account of coins].

147   Lloyd, T H (1977) *The English Wool Trade in The Middle Ages*:
       Cambridge University Press.

148   Clarke, Frank Wigglesworth (1888) *Weights, Measures and Money of All
       Nations*: [Published in USA].

149   Smith, Lucy Toulmin (Ed) (1894) *Expeditions to Prussia and to the Holy
       Land made by Henry, Earl of Derby (afterwards King Henry IV) in the
       years 1390–1 and 1392–2 being the Accounts kept by his Treasurer
       during two years*: Camden Society, New Series No LII.

150   Salzman, Louis Francis (1931) *English Trade in the Middle Ages*: Oxford
       University Press.

150A   Airy, Wilfred (1931) *English Trade in the Middle Ages*: Clarendon Press.

150B   Lipman, Vivian D (1961) *Three Centuries of Anglo-Jewish History*: Heffer.

150C   Evans, A (Ed) (1936) Pegolotti, Francesco Balducci; *La Practica della
       Mercatura*: Mediaeval Academy of America, Cambridge, Massachusets.

151   Garrett, Anne and Rowlinson, J S (translators) (1969) Danloux-Dumesnils,
       Maurice; *The Metric System*: University of London, The Athlone Press.

152   Stubbs, A J (1918) *Origin of the Metric System* [published in USA].

153 Lefebvre, Georges (1962) *The French Revolution from its Origins to 1793*: Routledge & Kegan Paul.

154 Bugge, Thomas (1969) *Science in France in The Revolutionary Era, Account of his stay in France 1789–1799*: M I T Press [translation].

155 MacDonald, Charles (1910) *The Metric System in Weights and Measures*: Royal Philosophical Society, Glasgow.

156 Martin, William (1794) *An Attempt to Establish Throughout His Majesty's Dominions a Universal Weight and Measure . . ..*: London.

157 Noel, Hon Edward (1889) *The Science of Metrology; or, Natural Weight . . ..*: E Stanford, London.

158 Atkinson, Llewelyn N B (1918) The Pros and Cons of the Metric System, *The Journal of the Institution of Electrical Engineers, Vol 56, No 271*.

159 McGreevy, Thomas (1953) *The MKS System of Units*: Pitman.

160 Symposium (1950) Papers on the MKS System of Units, *Journal of the Institution of Electrical Engineers* Vol 97, Pt 1.

161 McGreevy, Thomas (1964) Units, Giorgi and CGS Systems, *Encyclopaedic Dictionary of Physics, Vol 9*: Pergamon Press.

162 Boer, J de (1966) Short History of the Prefixes, *Metrologia, Vol 2 No 4*: p165–5.

163 Dresner, Stephen (1971) *Units of Measurement*: Harvey Miller and Medcalt Ltd, Aylesbury, Bucks.

164 Klein, Arthur H (1975) *The World of Measurement*: George Allen and Unwin Ltd.

165 Bell, R J and Goldman, David T (Eds) (1986) *SI The International System of Units*, [approved translation of *The International Bureau of Weights and Measures Publication: Le Systeme International d'Unites (SI)*]: National Physical Laboratory, Dept of Trade and Industry, HMSO.

166 Kibble, B P (October 1988) Redefining the Volt and the Ohm, *Institution of Electrical Engineers Review*: pp351–353.

167 *Metrologia*: Springer Verlag [English translation for the dates concerned].

168 Mellanby, K (1971) Letter in *Nature* 18 June 1971, *Environmental Pollution*: Monks Wood Experimental Station, Huntingdon.

169 Worley, N and Lewins J (Eds) (1988) *The Chernobyl Accident and its Implications for the United Kingdom*: (Published on behalf of the Watt Committee) Elsevier Applied Science Publishers.

170A (1984) *CIBS Code for Interior Lighting*: The Chartered Institution of Building Services.

170B (1991) *Five Years After Chernobyl: 1986–1991 a review*: The Watt Committee on Energy, London.

171   (1950) *Report of the Committee on Weights and Measures Legislation*: Cmnd 8219 [commonly called The Hodgson Report] HMSO.

172   (1964) *The Weights and Measures Act 1963*: with an introduction by John A O'Keefe: Butterworths.

173   (December 1966, reprinted 1967) *Decimal Currency in the United Kingdom*: presented to Parliament by the Chancellor of the Exchequer by Command of Her Majesty, Cmnd 3164 HMSO.

174   *Parliamentary Reports (Hansard) House of Commons Official Report*, Issues for the relevant dates: HMSO.

175   Ministry of Technology (1968) *Change to the Metric System in the United Kingdom. Report by the Standing Joint Committee on Metrication*: HMSO.

176   Vickers, Colonel J S (1969) *Making the Most of Metrication*: Gower Press, London.

177   Huntoon, R D (1967) *Science USA* [a USA periodical].

178   Schuler, A E (1960) Let's Quit Confusing Mass with Weight, *Journal of the Instrument Society of America*: 7 No 10 pp47–49.

179   *Metric News*: Swani Publishing Company, Rosco, Illinois [ceased publication in 1975].

180   *American Metric Journal*: Camarillo, California, USA.

181   Hopkins, Robert A (1975) *The International (SI) Metric System and How it Works*: AMJ Publishing Co, Tarzana, California, USA.

182   BS5555 (1981) *The International System of Units (SI)*.

183   BS5775 (1982) parts 0–15 *Letter Symbols and Abbreviations, Including ISO 31/0 – 1981*.

184   (1967) *World Weights and Measures*: United Nations Publications, New York.

185   Collar, George (1892) *Notes on the Metric System*: Macmillan & Co, London.

186   (1971) *Quantities, Units and Symbols*: A Report by the Symbols Committee of the Royal Society.

187   Clason, W E (1964) *Lexicon of International and National Units*: Elsevier Publishing Company [This handbook gives the names of all MKSA (now SI) units in ten leading languages].

188   Kennelly, A E (1928) *Vestiges of Pre-Metric Weights and Measures Persisting in Metric-System Europe*: New York.

189   Smith, James (c1825) *The Panorama of Science and Art; embracing the sciences . . . Vol II*: Henry Fisher at the Caxton Press, London p360.

190 Lunge, George (1910) *The Technical Chemists' Handbook*: Gurney and Jackson, London.

191 Feather, Robert (Ed) (1983–1992) *Weighing and Measuring*: Lincoln Publications, London.

Index of Persons Volume 2

Amery, Julian 306
Anne, Queen 334
Asquith, Herbert Henry 284
Balfour, Arthur James 282
Beaumont-Dark, A 316
Becquerel, Antoine Henri 260
Belhaven, Lord 280, 281
Bell, Roland 305
Benn, Sir Anthony Wedgwood 298, 303
Bottomly, Horatio 284
Bottomly, Peter 317
Bright, John 279
Burke, E 338, 357
Calder, Lord Ritchie 307
Campbell-Platt, Geoffrey 256, 258
Catalona, W 235
Celsius, Anders 216
Chamberlain, J Austin 284
Christen, J P 216
Cobden, Richard 276
Cohen, L 313
Colchester, Lord 281
Cumberland, R 345
Curie, Marie and Pierre 260
Denny, Sir Archibald, 285
Doppler, C J 412
Eden, Sir John 303, 308
Ewart, W 278
Feilden, Dr G B R 360
Ford, President G 329
Fraser, John 316
Frier, A 330
Gardiner, George 321
George, David Lloyd 284
Gibson, Thomas Milner 278

Gladstone, William Ewart 277
Gray, Louis Harold 260
Gray, Robert K 285
Guillaume, Charles 206
Hall, Joan 305
Halsbury, Earl of 291, 306
Haworth, D 283
Hodgeson, D 288, 290
Horton, J W 210
Isaacs, Rufus Daniel 284
Jay, Douglas 297
Keays, Colonel M de J 309
Kelly, E 284
Kelvin, Lord 215, 280, 283, 325
Kennelly, Prof A 209, 354
Kerby, Captain Henry 305
Kirwan, R 403
Lawson, Nigel 308
Leblond, A S 346, 349
Linacre, Vivian 321
Lunge, Prof George 353, 354
MacGregor, John 256
Mather, Carol 306
Maude, Francis 315, 316
Mellanby, Dr K 263, 358
Mohs, F 403
Morrison, W A 210
Norman, Sir H 283
Osborn, John A 305
Page, John 304, 308
Palmburg 216
Parker, H M 250
Parker, Thomas 285
Peyton, John 308, 310
Raven, R T 309

Reagan, President Ronald 332
Redmond, Robert 303
Renard, Colonel Charles 322
Rice, Spring (Lord Monteagle) 276
Richter, C F 401
Rippon, Geoffrey 302, 307
Robertson, Sir George Scott 284
Rothschild, Baron Lionel 276
Runciman, Walter 284
Schuler, A E 327
Scott (American astronaut) 331
Shepherd, Lord 306
Sievert, R M 260
Simpson, James 276
Smith, Giles 309
Smith, J E 279

Sørenson, S P L
Southard (Congressman) 326
Stenton, Lord 280
Stratton, Dr S W 326
Strauss, B S 282
Stubbs, A J 285
Thatcher, Margaret 310
Walkingame, F 358
Watt, James 281, 282
White, R 304
Wicksteed, J H 285
Williams, Alan 310
Winterton, M P 310
Wood, David 307, 308
Wrottesley, Sir John 276
Wynn, A H A 298

Index of Named Units

This index includes all the units in Volumes 1 and Volume 2 (excepting certain obscure and less consequential units)

Pages 1 to 200 are in Volume 1

Pages from 201 are in Volume 2

SI Units

The seven base units are starred thus: *
The two supplementary units are starred thus: **

*ampere 155, 156, 363
becquerel 250, 255, 389
*candela 220, 364
coulomb 155, 369
farad 155, 369
festmeter 205
gray 250, 256, 389
henry, 155, 370
joule 155
*kelvin 217, 364
*kilogram 147, 208, 336, 363
knot, international 244
lumen 271
lux 273

*metre 146, 153, 290, 325, 352, 363
*mole 158, 218, 221, 364
newton 156, 363
nit 274, 275
ohm 155, 225, 369, 377
pascal 268, 315
**radian 203, 219, 241, 364
*second 144, 210
siemans 369
sievert 260
**steradian 203, 219, 241, 364
volt 155, 371
watt 155, 227, 369
weber 156, 370

CGS Units

are 146, 225, 244, 373
bar 244, 268, 270, 374, 390
bayre 390
calorie 247, 374
curie 250, 389
degree centigrade (= Celsius) 165, 214, 216

dyne 243
erg 367, 368
fermi 244
gaede 390
gal 244
gauss 372

gilbert 372
gramme 352, 367
hectare 225, 244
litre 146, 205, 355, 366
maxwell 243, 370
oersted 243
phot 243
poise 243

rad 244, 250, 389
rem 244, 250, 389
rontgen 243, 250, 389
stilb 243, 274, 275
stokes 243, 368
torr 244, 268, 374

Other Named Units

acre 50, 83, 98, 118, 131
angstrom 153, 373
anker 138
atmosphere standard 269, 390
aune 96
avoirdupois pound 73, 91, 112, 128, 153
barleycorn 51, 84, 103, 136, 137
barn 204, 244, 315, 391
barrel 94, 116, 119, 130, 333, 388
bath 25
bega 31, 101
béká, beqa 30
berry 2
billion 228, 229, 268, 357, 360
bind of eels 76
bind of pelts 76
board foot 339, 379
boll 139
bovate 64
British thermal unit 214, 383
bushel 74, 80, 98, 113, 129, 168, 388
butt 116
byte 226
candle power 220, 270
caracute 63
carat 2, 3, 244, 404
cé 209
cental 164, 380
celo 392
chain 137, 378
chalder 139
chaldron 70, 379
char 71, 74, 75
choppin, chopyn 86, 127, 138
chudreme 138
clove 95, 130
coombe 129

cor 25
cord 170, 328, 379
cran 391
crannock 139
crowne 118
cubit 4–6, 15–18, 86, 124
daugh 137
daye worke 118
degree Fahrenheit 137, 214
degree Réaumur 215
denarius 54, 57
dicker 75
digit 3, 85
digitus 85, 140
direm 45, 60, 106
donum 392
drachma 20
dram 20, 106
droite 108
drop 138, 165
dunum 392
electron volt 243
elle 62, 83, 86, 162
eln 50
ephah 25
fast 113
farthing 57, 118, 407
fathom 6–8, 15, 86, 124, 131, 147, 378
feddan 392
fee 64
ferding 63
fillette 392
finger 6, 85, 122, 124
finquin 116, 139
firkin 116, 130
firlot 138, 161
fist 6

fluid ounce 333, 379
foot 18, 83, 85, 143, 155
forpit 138
fother 161
fotmal 74, 95, 96
funal 392
funiculus 140
furlong 50, 86, 123, 136, 378
gallon 74, 130, 138, 168, 388
gamma 244, 373
gerah 30
gill 86, 138, 379, 388
gon 315
grad 315
grade 242, 315
grain 43, 51, 101
gramos 354
granum 140
groat 87, 118
hand 20, 162
handbreadth 6, 20, 104
heap 113, 138
hide 50, 63, 131
hin 24
hobed 139
hogshead 116
homer 25
hon 24
horsepower 208, 371
hour 42
hundred (area) 50, 63
hundred (number) 75, 134, 392
hundredweight 66, 74, 86, 131, 161, 352, 380
inch 8, 19, 41, 85, 151, 352
iron, 378
jackpot 20
karat - see carat
kilderkin 116, 130
kilopond 242, 371
kip 392
kit 392
knot UK 382
kram 156
last 75
last of herrings 75
last of hides 75
last of wool 138

lete 63
li 23
libra 19, 41, 48, 70, 96, 134
line 136, 144
livre 143
llath 137
llathen 137
llestraid 137
log 24
lug, lugg, lugge 123
lusec 375
magnum 392
mancus 44, 48
mancuse 44
mark, marke, mark 48, 54, 79, 118, 135
mass unit 245
meiliaid 139
mercantile pound 66, 74, 115
merk 137
meshara 392
mil (see thou) 165, 204
mil (circular) 204, 388
mile 21, 98, 123, 137, 378
milliare 140
mina 30, 31, 33
mite 108
mouthful 20
mutchkin 86, 393
nail (of wool) 95
nail (unit of length) 122, 136
nautical mile 378
neper 393
noble 87, 118
noggin 393
nox 393
omer 25
ore 45, 47
ounce 91, 115, 352, 380, 388
oxgang, see bovate 64
pace 19, 86, 123
palm, see handbreadth 6, 20, 85
parsec 373
peck 114, 129, 138, 379, 388
pedwran 137
penny, silver 43, 45, 54, 66, 78, 90, 101, 409
pennyweight 45, 55, 89, 106, 108, 380
pfund 48, 59, 92, 144

pieze 375, 390
pim 30
pint 129, 134, 316, 379
pipe 116, 393
pot (Vol. 2)
pottle 86, 129, 130
pound, sterling 29, 47, 53, 336, 352, 380
poundal 383
punctum 140
pynte 149
quedet, qedet 31
quadrillion 230, 357, 360
quart 86, 111, 113
quarter, (capacity) 62, 74
quarter, (weight) 94, 108
quintal 222, 352, 374
quire 328
ream 328
remen 21, 22
ridge 137
rod, (pole, perch) 83, 118, 123, 177, 377
rood 118, 177, 378
royall 118
rundlett 116
sack 74, 75, 92, 95
sagene 166
sarpler 95
savart 393
scala 393
sceanta 45
screafall 139
seam 76, 138
second, (not of time) 144, 239
seed 2, 23, 24, 51
sheaf 139
shekel 29, 393
shilling 44, 54, 77, 78
sifta 63
slug 380, 382, 384
solanda 64
span, spanne 85, 122, 328
spit 394

stade 21
stadium 140
standard of timber 379
stang 139
stater 28, 72
stere 146, 206
sthene 374
stick of eels 76
stimpart 138
stone 66, 70, 74, 92, 138, 380
super 165
talent 29, 33
tertian 116
therm 316, 383
thou (0·001″) 165
third 144
thread 137
thumb 6, 85
timber 76
tod 95
tog 247, 248
toise 8, 14, 146, 355
ton 115, 352, 380
tonne 333, 353, 374
Tower pound 48, 54, 60, 73, 107, 115, 128
trillion 357
trip 163, 164
Troy ounce 54
troy pound 73, 105, 129, 134, 167, 171
truss 161
ulna yard 62, 83, 112
unga 138
Venice, weights 73, 100, 134
vergee 394
virga 140
virgate 63, 64
virgula 140, 141
wey (of wool) 47, 74, 138
wey (of cheese) 125
yard (ale) 394
yard (length) 60, 112, 137, 154, 155, 290

General Index Volume 2

abbreviations 222
absolute scale of temperature 215
alcohol (ethanol) tests 263
aluminium, in water 262
American Institute for Weights and
  Measures 326
American National Metric Council 328
American National Standards Institute 328
angle, grade system of measurement of 216
angle, radian 203, 219, 241
Apollo 15 moon mission 331
atmosphere, standard 270
atmospheric pollution 263
atmospheric pressures 269
atomic clocks 210, 212
Aurora Borealis 229
base units 202, 203
Beaufort scales of wind pressure 395–400
billion 228, 229, 268, 357, 360
black body 274, 405
blood lead 261
blood platelets 234
brasses, medieval 233, 234
British Standards Institution 296, 297, 416
British Weights and Measures Association
  284
caesium-133 212
caesium-134 255, 259
caesium-137 255, 258, 259
calendar
    Egyptian 209
    Ethiopian 209
    Gregorian 209
calorie, kilocalorie 214, 215
Camelford 262

Canada 267, 325, 340
Canada, metrication in 325, 340–2
carbon 218
carbon-12 221
carbon-14 259
carbon dating 259
carbon filament lamps 220
carbon monoxide 208, 263
car engines, power rating of 208
car exhausts catalysts 263
Carnot cycle 215
cé, decicé, millicé 209
c.g.s system of units 205, 326
Chernobyl 251–6, 259
Clostridium botulinum 256–8
codes of practice in SI 237
Comité International des Poids et Mesures
  (CIPM) 202, 211, 215, 241, 268, 363
compound prefixes 239
concentration 260
Confederation of British Industries (CBI)
  296, 302, 216
Conférence Générale des Poids et Mesures (CGPM) 202, 206, 211, 220
Congrès International de Chronomètre 209
Congrès International des Sciences Médicales 207
cost of delay in introducing metrication 286,
  318, 336
cost of metrication 286, 304, 305, 313, 317,
  328, 336
crystals – controlled oscillators 211
Customary System of Units (USA) 326,
  334, 387
day, mean solar 210

decillion 361
Decimal Association 276, 277, 283, 285
Decimal Association, News Bulletin of 285, 286
decimal coinage 276, 288, 409
Decimal Currency Act 1967 291, 292
Decimal Currency Act 1969 291, 293
Decimal Currency Board 346
decimal marker 345–50
density, relative 204, 205
dimensional analysis 416, 417
diodes, reverse-biased 220
dioptre 207
discharge lamps 272
earthquakes, Richter scale 401–2
EEC Directives 258, 261, 314–15, 318
efficacy of a lamp 272, 273
Egyptian year 209
emissivity 274
energy 226, 246–9
energy costs 249
ephemeris time 211
etalon standards 327
Ethiopia 209
European Court of Justice 321
Europe, pre-metric units 351–6
Federation for Small Businesses 321
filament lamps 272
films, thick and thin 234
fluorescent tube 272
fluoridated water 267
Food and Agriculture Organisation 225
Food and Drug Administration (USA) 267
Free Trade Agreement (FTA) 325
frequency 213, 364
frequency, rotational 213
fuel consumption of motor vehicles 351, 353
g (acceleration due to gravity) 242, 327
gas-filled lamps 272
General Accounting Office, United States 331
grade (system of angle measurement) 217
gravitational system of units 242, 327, 336
greenhouse gases 267
Greenwich Mean Time 212
half-life, of isotopes 359
Halsbury Report 293
hardness scale, Mohs', Kirwan's 403

heat flow 247. 248
Hodgson Report 288, 290
House of Lords 280–2
humidity, relative 405
ice 215
illuminance 217, 220, 270–5
illumination 220, 270–5
indentation, indentation tests 403
International Atomic Time 210, 212
International Civil Aviation Organisation 330
International Electrotechnical Commission (IEC) 202
International Organisation for Standardisation (ISO) 202, 329, 349
International System of Units (SI) 202
International Temperature Scale – see temperature
International Union of Pure and Applied Physics 223, 224
irradiance 273
irradiation of food 256
krypton-86 203
Lancashire textile industry 283–4
large numbers 356
lead contaminants 267, 268
lead in blood 261
lead weights, fishing 261
leap second 212
light, speed of 203
light year 229
locusts 228
luminance 274
luminous intensity 270, 364
mass 203, 207, 363, 364
maximum density of water 204
Mechanics Institutions 277
mercury contaminants 208, 267
mercury in thermometers 217
Metre Convention 201, 208
Metric America, Miss 1973 326
Metric Association (USA) 326
metrication, cost – see cost of metrication
Metric Board (USA) 329, 330, 332
metric practice in USA 339
metric system legalised (UK) 278–81, 290, 299, 311
metric system legalised (USA) 278, 290, 325, 329

metric teaching ruler 283
Metric Technical System (MTS) 242
Metric Weights and Measures Act 1864 279
Mexico 325, 343
milliard 228, 358
million 227, 357
mils, circular mils 204
MKSA system 213, 336
molality 221
molar 221
molarity 221
mole 203, 220, 364
moonlight 273, 275
multiples and submultiples of SI 222–36
nail sizes, USA 339, 340
nanotechnology 235
National Academy of Sciences (USA) 326
National Aeronautic and Space Administra-
    tion (NASA) 327, 331
National Bureau of Standards, USA 290,
    326, 327, 328
National Physical Laboratory (NPL) 202, 290
nitrates, in water 62, 267
nitrogen oxides 263
non-preferred submultiples 224, 225, 237
North American Free Trade Agreement
    (NAFTA) 325
oxygen demand, biological [biochemical] 262
ozone 263, 264
paper sizes 322–4
paper sizes, photographic 322–4
particulates (aerial contaminants) 263
partition coefficient 406
parts per billion (ppb) 264–6
parts per million (ppm) 266–8
pennies, Irish 277
pennies, new 291–5, 409
pennies, old 277, 407–8
perfect gas scale 216
pH 261, 411–12
piezo-electric effect 210
pips, on BBC time-signal transmission 212
plutonium 258
Poisson ratio 406
pollution, methods for specifying 260–6
pound sign £ 357
power 208, 368, 371, 373, 383
power stations 226, 227

practice, preferred and prohibited 237, 238
prefixes 235, 365
pressure 268–70, 383
Preston Institution for the Diffusion
    of Useful Information 277
pronunciation 343, 359–61
proof spirit 393
prostate-specific antigen 235
Provinces, Canadian 340
quadrillion 230, 360
quartz 218
quartz clock 210, 211
radiation, half life 259
radiation, ionising 249, 259
Rankine scale – see temperature
Réaumur scale – see temperature
recommended practice in SI 237–45
relative density 405
Renard series of numbers 321–2
Republican (French) year 209
resistance, thermal 248
resistors, electrical 225, 345
Revolution, French 209
road signs, metrication of 308, 310, 312,
    317, 339
rockets, specific impulse of 327
rotation, specific (plane polarized light) 393
salt 218
samples, sampling 419
screw threads 330
second, leap 212
Sellafield 234
Sèvres 201, 208
silica 218
Sizewell B electricity generator 227
Smiths Union Constitution 332
smog 263
spacing of symbols 239
Special Metric Panel of Aluminium
    Federation 309
specific heat capacity 375
specific rotation 393
spelling 227, 314, 337, 344
Statutory Instruments of 1994 318
substance, amount of (in chemistry) 220–1,
    364, 377
substance, amount of (in paper trade) 323–4
sulphur dioxide 264, 267

supplementary units of SI 203, 219, 364
Système International d'Unités (SI) 202,
    363–4
teeth, mottled 267
temperature intervals and scales,
    Celsius 214, 242, 247
    centigrade 214, 242
    Fahrenheit 214
    International Practical 217, 247, 364
    Kelvin 217, 363
    Palmburg 216
    Rankine 214, 215
    Réaumur 215
    thermodynamic 215, 217
terotechnology 224
thermal insulation of clothing 247
thermal resistivity 248
themisters 220
thermometers
    ethanol (alcohol)-in-glass 217
    liquid-crystal 220
    mercury-in-glass 217
    platinum resistance 220
time
    Coordinated Universal 212
    Ephemeris 210
    Greenwich Mean 212
    International Atomic 210, 212
    Universal (Mean Solar Time) 210–12
Tolerable Daily Intakes (TDIs) 268
torque 371, 375, 383

trillion, trillionth 230, 236, 356, 357
tungsten filament lamp 272
tyre pressures 269
Union of Pure and Applied Physics 223
United States National Bureau of Standards
    202
units, American (USA) 388
units, British 378
units, c.g.s. 367
units, metric technical 371
units of radiation (ionizing) 250–1, 389
units to be abolished 244
units to be tolerated, temporarily 244
USA Congress 210
vaccination, smallpox 338
variety reduction 321–2
vision, range and peak response (humans)
    235, 272
vitamins, destruction of 258, 266
War, First World (1914–1918) 272, 359
War, Second World (1939–1945) 217, 286,
    287, 289, 359, 409
water, potable 266, 268
water, triple point of 217
weather reports 269
Weights and Measures Act 1878 290
Weights and Measures Act 1963 290, 302
Weights and Measures Act 1985 319
World Health Organisation 262, 315
yard, standard, standardisation of 336

THE BASIS OF MEASUREMENT

VOLUME 1   HISTORICAL ASPECTS

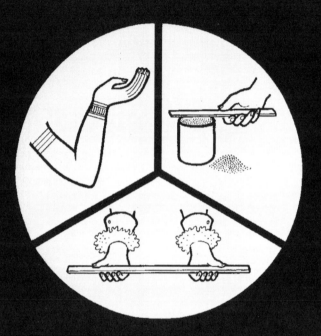

By THOMAS McGREEVY

Edited by Peter Cunningham

Contents – Volume 1

	General Acknowledgements	x
	Personal Acknowledgements	xi
	Editor's Acknowledgements	xii
	Preface	xiii
Chapter I	Some Ancient Units	1
Chapter II	Early English Units to the Early Tudor Period	43
	Early English Units 15th to 19th Century	100
Chapter III	Origin and Development of the Metric System	140
Chapter IV	Later English Units	159
	References and Further Reading	178
	Index of Persons Volume 1	189
	Index of Named Units	191
	General Index Volume 1	195

Tables – Volume 1

Table

I	Ratios between units – Ancient Egypt	6
II	Relationship of old and new Canon of Ancient Egypt	8
III	Numerical values of units in Ancient Egypt	16
IV	Units of Capacity in the Old Testament	27
V	Units of Mass in the Old Testament	30
VI	Ancient units in different Middle Eastern countries	31
VII	Subdivisions of the pound as at the reign of William I	53
VIII	Indentures and weights of silver pennies 1066–1464	90
IX	Units used in the English wool trade	95
X	Units of length, proposed by Gabriel Mouton	140

Illustrations – Volume 1

Frontispiece 1 Houses of Parliament before fire of 1834
Frontispiece 2 New Houses of Parliament, designed by Barry and Pugin

1 – Metrological divisions of the arm in ancient Egypt	4/5
2 – Grid for sculpture used in ancient Egypt	9
3 – The tangent square of Marcus Vitruvius Pollio	12
4 – The tangent square, Leonardo da Vinci version	13
5 – Ancient Egyptian etalon cubit of Amenempht (Museum of Turin)	17
6 – The double remen of ancient Egypt	22
7 – Principle of moments applied to lever weighing machines	32
8 – Ancient Egyptian equal-arm balances	35
9 – Roman balance of Vespasian (Museum of Turin)	36
10 – Graph showing balance conditions for a bismar	38
11 – The earliest known illustration of a bismar	39
12 – Early English silver coins	46
13 – Basis of Saxon land area	49
14 – Exchequer Standard Winchester bushel of Henry VII	49
15 – Etalon yard bars of Henry VII and Elizabeth I	111
16 – English standard wine gallon Queen Anne (= present USA gallon)	126
17 – Line and end standards for etalons of length – diagram	126
18 – Tresca etalon metre bar – cross section (1874–1879)	152
19 – Heaped and stricken measures	152
20 – Set of nested brass weights – diagram	174
21 – Laboratory weights – mid 20th century	175
22 – Laboratory spring balance and force-meter – mid 20th century	176
23 – Arithmetic tables from school exercise book, 1930s	177